Family Work for Schizophrenia

A Practical Guide

LIZ KUIPERS
JULIAN LEFF
DOMINIC LAM

Family Work for Schizophrenia
A Practical Guide

GASKELL

British Library Cataloguing-in-Publication Data
Kuipers, Liz
    Family Work for Schizophrenia: Practical Guide
    I. Title
    616.89

ISBN 0-902241-49-4

Distributed in North America
by American Psychiatric Press, Inc.
ISBN 0-880486-16-3

The views presented in this book do not necessarily reflect
those of the Royal College of Psychiatrists, and the publishers
are not responsible for any error of omission or fact.

Printed in Great Britain by Henry Ling Limited, Dorchester, Dorset

"Don't turn your back"

Don't turn your back on my brother
Just because he does not fit
into your world.
His torment is real
and he would change it if he could.

His illness is not something
you can see
but is real, all too real,
nonetheless,
and the boy we know is lost to us.
Like a missing child
the pain never dies
but haunts us with hopes
that some day
we will find him again.

An excerpt from a poem by Barbara Bingham. Reprinted with the author's permission from the *World Schizophrenia Fellowship Newsletter*, September 1991.

The authors

Liz Kuipers is Senior Lecturer in Clinical Psychology at the Institute of Psychiatry, London, and Honorary Consultant Psychologist, Bethlem Royal Hospital and Maudsley Hospital, London; she was formerly Member of Scientific Staff, Medical Research Council Social and Community Psychiatry Unit, Institute of Psychiatry, London

Julian Leff is Director of the Medical Research Council Social and Community Psychiatry Unit and Professor of Social and Cultural Psychiatry at the Institute of Psychiatry, London, and Honorary Consultant Psychiatrist, Bethlem Royal Hospital and Maudsley Hospital, London

Dominic Lam is Lecturer in the Department of Psychology, Institute of Psychiatry, London; he was formerly Member of Scientific Staff, Medical Research Council Social and Community Psychiatry Unit, Institute of Psychiatry, London

Contents

Acknowledgements

We would like to thank all the families we have met and talked to over the years, for their contribution, insights and humour even in the most difficult situations. They taught us a great deal about coping with problems.

We are very grateful to the 20 psychiatric nurses who completed our first two training courses in family work for schizophrenia. They taught us a great deal about how to teach. Dr Peter Burnett and Mrs Ellen Wheeler joined our discussions throughout the writing of this book and made many valuable contributions from the viewpoints of a family therapist and a carer, respectively. We wish to acknowledge with gratitude the major role played by Dr Ruth Berkowitz in developing and shaping our form of family work during the many years she was a member of our team. An excellent standard of typing by Mrs Yvonne Waters smoothed the production of the manuscript.

1 Introduction to our approach

From the late 1960s to early 1970s, researchers at the Medical Research Council's Social Psychiatry Unit in London were investigating whether family atmosphere can influence the course of illness in schizophrenia. They found that patients living with a critical or overinvolved relative were more prone to relapse. They coined the term 'high expressed emotion' to describe such families (Brown & Rutter, 1966; Brown *et al*, 1972). These findings were replicated first in the Medical Research Council's Unit using a shorter interview schedule by Vaughn & Leff (1976). Since then further replications have been reported throughout the world and in different cultures (e.g. Vaughn *et al*, 1984; Jenkins *et al*, 1986; Leff *et al*, 1987). More recently, however, there have been a few reports that did not replicate the earlier findings. Parker & Hadzi-Pavlovic (1990) summarised the recent controversial studies.

'Expressed emotion' (EE) is essentially a clinical concept. It contributes little to our understanding of the aetiology of the illness, but is a robust predictor of the course of the illness when someone with schizophrenia lives with relatives. The model of treatment described in this manual stems from this predictive power of EE.

In our research and in our clinical work we have selected families in which at least one member is rated as 'high EE'. This does not imply that low-EE families are not in need of help, only that high-EE families have a higher priority, and we have to be selective when trained therapists are in short supply. We are in the process of setting up a national training network for family work with schizophrenia, which is aimed primarily at psychiatric nurses. However, any psychiatric professional could benefit from the training. This *Practical Guide* forms part of the training materials, which also include video-tapes and a training manual. Training in the use of the Camberwell Family Interview (CFI; Brown & Rutter, 1966) and the EE rating scales is not part of the course, since we view these techniques as mainly for use in research studies.

Most services will be in the position of having to concentrate resources on the families in greatest need. In the absence of ratings of relatives' EE, such families can be identified by the following rules of thumb:

(a) relatives living with patients who relapse more often than once a year despite being compliant with maintenance neuroleptics
(b) relatives who frequently contact staff for reassurance or help
(c) families in which there are repeated arguments leading to verbal or physical violence; and any family that calls in the police
(d) a single relative, usually the mother, looking after a schizophrenic patient on her own.

Our model of treatment is highly specific and consists of a psycho-educational component and a structured family approach, with an emphasis on cognitive–behavioural techniques. It is known that educating relatives about the illness and working with them to tackle some of their problems attenuates their critical or overinvolved behaviour, hence preventing relapses (see, for example, Leff *et al*, 1982, 1985, 1989, 1990; Tarrier *et al*, 1988).

The following are the basic assumptions and philosophy of the treatment model:

(a) Schizophrenia is conceptualised as an illness with a biological origin. A diathesis–stress model is used to explain how, in a vulnerable person, stresses such as unexpected life changes might bring on the illness or a relapse.
(b) Instead of the relatives being blamed, they are enlisted as therapeutic agents, in order to help the patients. Furthermore, the burden and stress of living with a schizophrenic patient are taken seriously.
(c) There is an emphasis on openness and working in partnership with the family. Information about the illness is shared. In doing so the therapists also admit that there is a lot about the illness that is not known. Collaboration is elicited by mutual work on goal setting, prioritising, and task setting.
(d) Families are seen to have needs and strengths. A positive approach is used to build on the families' strengths in order to tackle their problems.
(e) The psychosocial family intervention described here is offered as part of a package, in conjunction with drugs and out-patient management. There is no attempt to substitute traditional management with family treatment.

Differences between our approach to work with families and that of others

People began to work with families in the early 1950s. At first, the focus was on families with a schizophrenic member, but it soon broadened to include families with the whole range of psychiatric conditions. The earliest work was based on psychoanalytic theory; however, in recent years this approach has been eclipsed by the rise of systemic family therapy.

The work we describe in this manual belongs to neither of these schools, although it has borrowed ideas and techniques from the systemic approach. The differences between our mode of working and the others are worth spelling out.

(a) The disease concept of schizophrenia

There are a number of psychoanalytic theories which trace the origin of schizophrenia to disturbed parent–child relationships. Within this tradition, schizophrenia is viewed as a purely psychological disturbance which is explicable in terms of the disturbance induced in the child by the parents.

The systemic view is rather different, since schizophrenia is seen as the presentation by one member of a 'mad' family situation. The madness characterises the whole family system, in which one member is 'chosen' to present it to the professional. This person is often referred to as 'the designated patient', with the implication that the pathology lies in the whole family.

In contrast to the above approaches, we consider that schizophrenia is a biological illness of the brain that can occur in families which are functioning perfectly well.

(b) The role of the family

It is evident from the above that both psychoanalytic and systemic theories implicate the family in the causation of schizophrenia. We consider that families do not exert a *causal* influence, although they can modify the *course* of the illness.

(c) The aim of therapy

In both psychoanalytic and systemic family therapy, the aim is to correct presumed family dysfunction. The family is consequently the client of the therapists. We do *not* view the family as in need of treatment. Hence we avoid calling our interventions 'family therapy'. Our aim is to help the family to cope better with the sick member who is suffering from a defined disease. We see the family as an ally in treating the schizophrenic patient.

(d) The role of insight

In psychoanalytic, but not systemic, family therapy, the insight of the therapist is fed back to the family in the form of interpretations to effect change. Although we value a psychodynamic understanding of family relationships, we do not make interpretations to the family. We have found that in families with a schizophrenic member they fail to produce change.

(e) The role of the therapists

In traditional psychoanalytic therapy, the therapist avoids answering direct questions and does not offer advice. We set out to give the family information, advice, and guidance. However, we do not expect the family to be a passive recipient of these. Instead, we encourage the family to take an active part in discussing the information provided and to work with us to find solutions to their problems. In addition, we are active on behalf of the family in negotiating with various services to help to engage them with the family. This would not be undertaken by a traditional psychoanalyst, although a systemic therapist might work with external agencies as part of the larger system within which the family operates.

General interpersonal effectiveness

The model of therapy being used here emphasises the importance of rapport (a good and harmonious working relationship) with families. To be consistent with our family work model, the therapists should never criticise or blame the family. Apart from being an undesirable role model for the relatives, any criticism is likely to be passed on to the patient. The Rogerian principles of therapists being warm, empathic and genuine are seen as crucial for effective working with families. Therapists should show adequate warmth towards individuals in families as human beings in need of help. Empathy is defined as the ability to understand accurately the perspectives of other people. It is different from sympathy, which is the sharing of or having compassion for another individual's pain. It could be argued that too much sympathy could make therapists lose their objectiveness and hence ability to help. Furthermore, therapists should be genuine, open and sincere with families. Any unrealistic or unmet promise would be judged by families as insincere.

Therapists should not adopt an authoritarian attitude nor impose the official view of schizophrenia on families. There is an important distinction between making factual statements about what we know regarding the illness and being insensitive and authoritarian. Moreover, it is important to elicit families' views regularly to gain their collaboration. Family members' feelings, experiences, strengths and needs should be respected. Families' past or present attempts to cope, no matter how undesirable they may be to the therapists, should be respected as their best effort to cope given their resources.

The premise of our model is that these interpersonal qualities are necessary but not sufficient for a good therapeutic outcome. The techniques described in this treatment model are enhanced when carried out in a good therapeutic relationship. If not, therapy can be seen as robotic, and families would think that the therapists do not care about or understand them. Considerable skill is required to convey a good and caring professional attitude. The degree of warmth and genuineness being expressed by the therapists is important. But one could argue that the amount of warmth and genuineness perceived by individual family members is more important. The way to find out is by asking for regular feedback. Perhaps one of the best ways to learn how to convey these qualities initially is to observe how your more experienced colleagues do it.

Support group for therapists

Work with families with a schizophrenic member is emotionally demanding. We have found that therapists benefit from having a support group of their peers which meets about once a month. This may not always be feasible, but should be given high priority. Guidelines on how to run such a group will be found in our *Training Manual for Therapists* (available from the authors).

Summary

We conceptualise schizophrenia as a biological illness which makes the patient sensitive to stress. Consequently our therapeutic approach involves drug treatment in conjunction with family work. Families are seen as partners of the therapists in an alliance to help the patients. We do not blame the relatives for the illness, nor do we view the family as in need of treatment. Therapists should be warm and empathic, but also need to work actively with the family on their problems. Therapists benefit from having their own support group.

2 Engaging the family

The intervention is a package composed of a variety of types of work with the family. The three basic components are:

(a) an education programme
(b) family sessions in the home
(c) a relatives' group.

The intervention begins with the education programme, then family sessions are arranged. Additionally relatives may be invited to attend a group, which can be run in parallel with the family sessions.

It is very likely that a family will be reluctant to engage in treatment sessions. There may have been a history of unhelpful previous professional contact, actual or perceived. Relatives may feel blamed for the illness and worry that treatment will pinpoint this. There is often a very real fear that any change will make things worse, not better, and that the status quo, even with all its problems, is, after all, to be preferred. Finally there may be an atmosphere of resignation which can set in after many years; a feeling that 'nothing can be done', so that offering help is a waste of everyone's time.

Clinical example
This illustrates the family's dissatisfaction with previous professional contacts and a sense of resignation. (In all the clinical examples, T stands for therapist, M and F for mother and father, H and W for husband and wife, and P for the patient.)

M. They let him out because he was malicious. That's what they told me. I mean they don't have to deal with him if they choose to. But guess where he went. He came straight home and I had to deal with it all. I rang up the ward and that girl said she was scared of him. I mean there were so many of them and they were scared. What about me? And they gave him a week's supply of drugs. This is the first time they did that since my last showdown with them. If he takes an overdose this time, I would hold the hospital responsible. I sometimes wonder if things are ever going to get any better.

We do know that people are more likely to accept help at a time of crisis, for example after an admission to hospital. If there is an adamant refusal, therapists may have to wait until a future crisis to try again.

Engaging the family is the first task: unless a family's reluctance to engage is tackled, then however skilled the intervention, it will not be taken up. Therapists must be aware that every professional contact with the family, each telephone call, or chat in the corridor, is part of this engagement process and it should not be done in an off-hand way.

It helps to remember that most families will have many needs, and that if they can be engaged then these are likely to be addressed. Engagement consists of offering positive, pleasant, polite contact, while sharing appropriate care and concern for the family's problems. This must be offered consistently, despite a family's negative response. They may refuse contact, avoid appointments, turn up late or not at all, or make it difficult to arrange a firm time; when a time has finally been arranged a crucial family member may decide to go out.

There is an advantage in beginning with the education programme since the therapists are offering something families are often desperate for – information. Furthermore, the fact that the therapists are prepared to make the effort to visit the home in order to give the family information aids the process of engagement.

The only situations in which we have found it impossible to engage a family have been when patients have been so suspicious of the therapist, or have specific paranoid ideas, that they refuse to allow access to the relative. One wife was terribly jealous of any contact her husband had, and the family felt too worried to accept a visit. These worries have to be respected and help offered later, when the ideas may be less prevalent.

Strategies

The general strategy for engagement is to offer positive contact, at the pace which the family will allow. Persistence is often necessary, as refusal of first contact is common. Being flexible as to time and place of a visit, not becoming angry when arrangements break down, and continuing to offer another contact will often enable enough trust to be built up for the family to risk a meeting.

It may be helpful to meet informally before family work begins so that a family feel they have some prior knowledge of who you are and what you are like. Sometimes, of the two therapists (see Chapter 4), one at least will have had contact before. One may have met the patient while they were acutely ill in the hospital, so that the patient may be able to introduce the therapist to the rest of the family. A relative while visiting may have been greeted by a therapist. It is important that these early, informal contacts are pleasant and reassuring. It is not going to help a family engage if there have been previous angry or hostile exchanges in the corridor.

Families that refuse

If the family continues to refuse contact there may come a point when this has to be accepted, and help offered at a later stage. However, there are some strategies to try first.

If neither of the therapists knows the family, they should try to get introduced informally by a trusted third party who can be reassuring about their involvement. It can help to have some short statements in mind as to their reason for wanting to work with the family: "We would like to see how you're all getting on now that John is coming home soon," "We want to find out how things are at the moment and see if we can help you with any problems that may arise".

Sometimes it can help to meet the family singly; a first meeting may be with one relative alone. Once this contact has been made, it is important to make it clear that you would like to meet all those who have reasonably close contact with the patient (live in the same house, visit frequently, are key members such as parents or spouses). Separate letters to all relatives stating time and date of the next meeting have been found to be useful. It cannot be assumed that family members will pass on messages, and an individual letter is likely to be received and read. It is important to convey to the family that it would be helpful for everyone to attend who is or has been involved in the caring for the patient.

Occasionally the patient will not engage. Usually this is connected to acute phases of the illness, but sometimes a patient will feel that listening to relatives' complaints will not be productive. Make it clear to the patient that everyone will have a say in a family meeting, and all problems can be aired and listened to. It is then important to stick to these rules.

For some families, despite all efforts, only part of the family system will engage. It is important to work with whosoever will attend; they can become advocates and persuade other family members to join in. It is worth keeping the channels open and continuing to ask if absent family members would like to join meetings. Often, after many months, they will. However, even if only one or two family members accept the help it should still be offered; it is possible, though often more difficult, to effect change through part of the family system, and therapists should always be prepared to do so.

Maintaining families in treatment

Once the family has come to attend the first family session, one of the main tasks for the therapists is to maintain them in treatment. Some families might have had bad experiences with help from professionals in the past, but have come with scepticism about the present offer of help. Others might hold different or unrealistic expectations of therapy. Families who have tried to cope for years might feel pessimistic about the future, but have decided to find out what the therapists have to offer this time. Hence it is extremely important to explore the families' past experience of professional help, their expectation of therapy this time, and their pessimism. It is a delicate balance between infusing hope and conveying what realistically can be expected from therapy. Empathy, warmth and genuineness help. In addition, the therapists should convey the message that this type of family work has been found repeatedly to prevent relapses, and spell out that change would be slow and gradual. They should also express their willingness to work with the family.

Sometimes families will not acknowledge any positive changes. Therapists are cautioned not to argue and attempt to prove their therapeutic efficacy, as these families are likely to respond by showing the therapists that they are wrong. Instead, the therapists should reiterate that changes are slow. Attempts should be made to understand why these families are frightened to admit that change has occurred.

During treatment, therapists should make clear the purpose of behavioural goals and relate them from time to time to what the family want to achieve ultimately, so that they understand the small steps involved. Regular feedback, either verbally or in writing (e.g. 'Helpful Aspects of Therapy' forms – see Appendix 2), helps to elicit how families see the way treatment is going. Another important aspect of therapy is to hold regular reviews with families to explore how they feel about treatment. Any dissatisfaction or pessimism can then be dealt with before families decide to end treatment prematurely.

Summary

Families are likely to be difficult to engage in treatment. Therapists need to be aware of this, to be prepared to be persistent, and to continue to offer help even if it is initially rejected. We would always try to work with part of the family and aim to engage the others in due course. Contact may be initiated at times of crisis, or through informal meetings. Reminding families that progress will be slow helps to maintain them in treatment.

3 Being a therapist, not a guest

Social pressures

The fact that sessions are held in patients' homes rather than in a professional location needs special consideration. People who come to see professional staff in their own offices accept the unwritten rules that govern professional consultations. By contrast, staff visiting a home, particularly when they ask to see the whole family, are in an ambiguous position. Are they to be treated as professionals or guests? The family may wish to treat them as guests for a number of reasons. They are likely to be grateful that the staff have made the effort to come to them and may wish to express their gratitude by offering hospitality. The influence of culture should not be ignored in this area. The further east one travels, the more importance is given to the idea of the guest as a person to be honoured and respected. It should be recognised that families from different cultural backgrounds will differ in their attitudes towards a member of staff entering their home.

Family members may try to turn the visit into a social occasion to avoid working on the problems they experience. Therapists have to be wary of these attempts, as it is easy to be diverted from the main purpose of the visit. It is understandably more comfortable to settle into a social role than to steer the family firmly in the direction of hard work.

Family members are often socially isolated from friends and relatives outside the home. The therapists may be seen as welcome company to relieve loneliness. This can also lead to pressure from family members to adopt a social role.

Forms of address

The problems around establishing a therapeutic role start at the very beginning, when the therapists introduce themselves to the family. How should they refer to themselves – by their first name, their surname, or both, and should they use a professional title (e.g. doctor) if they have one? How should they address family members – Mr and Mrs so and so, or first names? There are no hard and fast rules, and therapists should adopt a style with which they are comfortable. However, there are a few guidelines. The two co-therapists need to establish an egalitarian relationship with each other and will want to talk to each other and refer to each other by name in front of the family. They will certainly want to address each other directly by first name, and it will appear odd and unnatural if they refer to each other by surname or title when talking to the family.

When working with a parental family, one of the aims will be to reinforce intergenerational boundaries and the authority of the parents. This can be helped by addressing the parents as Mr and Mrs so and so. They will certainly refer to their son or daughter by their first name, so the therapists will need to follow suit. Parents may ask the therapists to call them by their first names, in which case it would be churlish to refuse. With a married couple the therapists should begin by using Mr and Mrs but should switch to first names if requested.

Greeting and parting

At the beginning of a session, when the therapists enter the home, it is customary to exchange pleasantries. However, this should not be allowed to go on too long. The therapists need to get down to the business of the visit within the first few minutes. A good way to start is to ask a general question about how things have been since the last visit. The therapists should then work their way round to asking about the task that was set at the end of the previous session.

Sessions should last for a certain length of time (usually an hour), which the family should be informed of. The duration of the sessions should be kept to reasonably closely, but not rigidly. The therapists need to work towards getting the family to agree on a homework task by the end of the session. On leaving there is likely to be another exchange of pleasantries, but the therapists must make sure that all family members are aware of the date and time of the next session.

Tea and biscuits

Some families regularly offer tea or coffee during a session, while with others this may happen from time to time. The therapists should start by assuming that the offer of a hot drink is customary and innocuous. There is usually no harm in accepting, and it may help the family feel that they are doing something to express their gratitude. However, the timing of the offer should be carefully considered. It may occur at a point in the session when it is clearly diversionary. In this case the therapists should thank the family member but ask if it could be postponed.

Another useful strategy can be used in a parental family in which the mother always makes the drinks. The patient can be asked to take on the task from time to time, thus preventing the mother's avoidance tactics and giving the patient an opportunity to demonstrate his/her competence.

Biscuits are often offered along with tea or coffee, which is acceptable, but some family members have been known to bake cakes specially for the therapists' visits. This has to be judged within the cultural context of the family, and if considered to be excessive should be politely but firmly discouraged.

Alcoholic drinks should never be accepted, as overstepping the bounds of ordinary hospitality and possibly impairing the therapists' efficiency.

Personal questions

Personal questions to the therapists may represent genuine curiosity or may be another way of socialising the visit. While refusal to answer any personal questions is likely to give an impression of rudeness, therapists should be wary of going into any detail about their personal lives. Failure to observe caution will open the way to increasing socialisation of the therapists' visits and undermining of working relationships.

Summary

Working in a patient's home subjects the therapists to unaccustomed social pressures. Therapists must ensure that they are able to maintain a working relationship with the family, while avoiding being uncivil.

4   Co-therapy

For this form of family work we do recommend that therapists work in pairs. We have always found it helpful to have two people, to plan the family session, discuss what happened, and decide what to do next. During a session it is an advantage to have one of you observing while the other is talking, and vice versa.

However, working with someone else means that there is a relationship between you; this has to be constructive and any problem looked at to prevent difficulties.

Modelling

A pair of therapists provide a model for the family. Two disparate people are trying to work together to improve things – they may not agree and they may not work in the same way. The way these differences are acknowledged and resolved may be the first indication that a family has had for many years that different viewpoints can be discussed. Modelling negotiating skills is a useful aspect of co-therapy. Acknowledging and discussing differences openly can help the family to learn how to do this without anger. Do not try to do it, however, unless you know that you will manage it positively. Many families have been caught in repetitive and conflict-generating patterns that they cannot sort out. Therapists must make sure that they do not do the same.

Trust

Working with someone else means that the relationship has to incorporate trust and cooperation; you have to feel comfortable enough with your co-therapist to trust their judgement and be able to reinforce what they do or suggest. This is the model to aim for. There is no point in starting to work with a family with a partner whom you intensely dislike or disapprove of. You must respect each other's skills and be able to offer support to each other. However, even with a trusted partner there will be times, during family sessions, when you feel angry, dislike what was done or feel your skills were neglected. Use a debriefing session to air these feelings and sort them out. If necessary, ask for outside supervision or help. Do not let actively negative feelings between you surface during the session. It is likely that you yourselves will be recreating family conflicts, and that the anger and dislike are reflections of the family dysfunction. However, your role is to defuse conflict and not to perpetuate it.

Forming alliances

Working collaboratively and constructively does not imply that you both have to do the same thing in a session. Often it is helpful to work together, to take up and agree points the other has made. There are other times when it can be helpful to work with separate parts of the family system. You may want to enforce generation boundaries, so one of you will work with the parents, voicing their concerns, making sure their view is heard; the other may work with the patient, acknowledging the problems, helping them put their ideas across. These 'alliances' can ensure that parts of the family are not alienated or neglected. However, such alliances should be flexible. It should be possible to change them if necessary. Otherwise family members can feel that *only one* therapist understands them.

Working on separate tasks

Sometimes it can be helpful to split tasks. When giving the education one of you has to read it and the other can usefully pick up the problems and emotional issues that the family raises. One therapist may have particular expertise that the family may ask for – information on benefits, on medication, on decisions that the 'team' has been involved in; it is helpful to use this knowledge and for one of you to supply the answer.

Planning sessions

Before a session starts, take some time with your co-therapist to plan the detail of what you will do. The important thing here is to have a small number of joint aims and some idea of how to achieve them. Sessions can never be planned absolutely; families may have a pressing problem to discuss which will take priority. It is also necessary to be spontaneous and react to the nuances of family functioning, so that families know that you are listening and responding to their problem and not to some predetermined list. However, it is helpful to decide who will start the session, what you will try to achieve, and when it will finish.

Support during the session

During a session, it is likely that you will feel stuck at some stage. You may not know what to do. You may suddenly feel that the discussion is missing the point or that a difficult emotional issue has been raised. Use your co-therapist at this point in the session. It is helpful to admit openly, to think aloud, that you have a problem and to consult with your partner over what should happen next. This consultation is a more overt part of what should be happening between you; you should both be aware of each other's input and be able to check that the next suggestion is one to pursue.

Sometimes it may be necessary to rescue each other. One therapist may be diverted by the family, put off the point, or persuaded into an irrelevant discussion. The other therapist must be alert to these possibilities and be prepared to make an intervention that pulls the family back to the task or aim of the session.

Debriefing

At the end of a session make sure you both leave time to discuss what happened. If one or both of you rushes off, it can sometimes leave quite intense feelings of concern or anxiety that are carried round. Make sure that these concerns are brought out immediately, dealt with in some way, and a decision made about the next meeting.

Summary

Working with a co-therapist is recommended, but requires that the relationship is positive and constructive, and models negotiating skills. Two people working together allows alliances to be made and tasks to be split. The relationship requires trust for any conflict to be dealt with, if necessary using outside supervision. Co-therapy is more effective if sessions are planned together beforehand, therapists support each other during a session, and sufficient time is allowed for debriefing afterwards.

5   Offering education

Clinical example

This illustrates relatives' need for information. This woman's daughter had been ill for eight years and was on biweekly injections.

M. You see when I went to the doctor for the doctor to tell me what is it, I expected the doctor to say "Oh, Coral suffers from schizophrenia. You must watch her behaviour pattern, you must be careful because she suffers from this. She will do this or she will do that – whatever." But nothing. Nobody said anything to me. Nobody.

The education programme

The material is in the form of a booklet published by the National Schizophrenia Fellowship (Appendix 1). The topics are: symptoms of schizophrenia, its cause and course, and its treatment.

The education is given in two sessions in the home, working through two sections of the booklet on each occasion. It is usual to give the programme while the patient is still in hospital, so that only the relatives are present. The booklets are left with the relatives, who are told they should decide whether to give them to the patient to read. This has been standard practice, but recently patients have been more actively involved in education by therapists, either individually or with the relatives. If the patient is to be educated with the relatives, some preparation may be needed, particularly a discussion of the diagnosis and why it is being made.

The material from the booklets is read out exactly as it is written; however it is interspersed with comments which tailor it to the patient's particular situation. In order to be able to do this, the therapist has to become familiar with the patient's range of symptoms and the family history beforehand. For example, "He may hear voices talking to him or about him. I think that has happened to John hasn't it?" "Many arguments can arise over his personal cleanliness. I think, though, that John has always kept himself neat and clean."

The therapist should tell the family members before starting that there will be plenty of time to ask questions, and should pause after each statement to allow the family to respond. Some families will need encouragement to ask questions, make statements, or voice their disagreement with various items of information. The therapist must be prepared to enter into discussion with the family, clarifying the position established by the information in the booklets but listening to and trying to understand the family's view. On no account should the therapist attempt to impose the 'official' view on the family.

Clinical example
This illustrates the importance of listening to the family's view and not imposing the 'official' view.
T. That's what we call it, schizophrenia. What do you call your problem, David?
P. Em, I don't know. I don't know what it is. Depression I suppose that's what it's called. If the professor is saying to me. . . . I mean, he didn't say to me that you've got schizophrenia. He just said you are ill, or he just said he thought you had an illness. But, em, if he had said to me that you had schizophrenia, I would be quite concerned because, you know, I need to be treated for it. It seems to be more of a dangerous illness than what I seem to have at the moment. I really needed to be in hospital longer or be under his guidance a little bit longer. But he hadn't said that.
T. I think that maybe we need to address what people feel about the kind of problems that you have got. It is very much similar to what we would term as schizophrenia. Now you may have a different term for that or a different name. That's fine. But I think it may be useful to actually go through some of these things. I think there are often a lot of fantasies or things that people have heard about schizophrenia that actually aren't true in many ways. So should we press on?
P. But it doesn't seem that they are quite clear. It just seems that schizophrenia doesn't seem to have any kind of patterns. It's an illness that just affects people differently. And it may not be the same illness that causes schizophrenia. It just seems to be all over the place really. You might not get it again.
T. I suppose like with most problems, you may get a core of things that you can say are principally the same or similar. But of course we are all individuals and the way that we respond to a particular illness is bound to be dependent on our individual personalities. And so the way that we become ill obviously is very much a representation of how we are as a person, so to speak. It will be very different for everybody.
P. So it's down to the individual really, the illness.

The long-term process of education

The education programme is only the very beginning of a process of education which will continue throughout the therapists' contact with the family. The family's view of the patient's condition is unlikely to change in response to the education sessions, but usually shifts gradually, over a year or so. Family members will repeatedly ask the same questions of the therapists over a long time. The therapists need to be patient in repeating the same information and in negotiating with family members over the differences between their views of the patient's condition and the 'official' version. When a resolution of differences is achieved the questions about that area usually cease. However, a new crisis will often precipitate a resurgence of questions. It must be recognised that even if family members accept most of the information, they rarely change their beliefs about causation.

The main topics

In each area of the education programme there are two main points that the therapist needs to emphasise. They are as follows:

- (a) Causation
  - (i) The family is not to blame for the illness.
  - (ii) Inheritance plays a part, but there are other causes which have yet to be discovered.
- (b) Negative symptoms
  - (i) The negative symptoms are caused by the illness and are not under the patient's control.
  - (ii) They do not respond to drugs but will gradually improve over one to two years.
- (c) Prognosis
  - (i) One in four people who develop schizophrenia will recover completely and remain well for years.
  - (ii) Most of the remainder will improve and can lead relatively normal lives outside of hospital.
  It is important to give the family hope.
- (d) Treatment and management
  - (i) The illness makes patients sensitive to stress, which should be reduced where possible in order to benefit both patient and relatives.
  - (ii) Drugs help in the long term, but it is also important that the atmosphere is calm and predictable.

It is no use telling family members not to be critical or overinvolved. People cannot simply stop behaving in a particular way in response to advice, especially if they are driven by emotion. They will perceive this as criticism of themselves and it will make them less likely to engage with the therapists. The therapists will work with them to help change these attitudes over long periods of time. However, it is important for the family to understand what the goals are, namely a calm rather than argumentative atmosphere, predictable rather than inconsistent attitudes, and support and tolerance rather than rejection.

Following the second education session, the therapists offer to come regularly to help the family tackle the problems of everyday life with a schizophrenic member.

Summary

Education about schizophrenia is given in two sessions in the relatives' home. It covers the causes, symptoms and prognosis of schizophrenia, and the treatment and management. It is tailored to the individual patient's symptoms and circumstances. It is only the beginning of a process of learning about the illness that continues throughout work with the family.

6   Family sessions

Any social group has a structure. This applies to families, in which the structure is usually organised around parent–child and husband–wife relationships. These vary with era and culture; for instance, the conventional image of the father as the head of the household is disappearing among middle-class white people, whereas it remains intact in many Asian families in Britain. Furthermore, there is an increasing number of single-parent households in which the mother carries full parental responsibility. These variations have to be borne in mind when assessing the structure of the family you are going to work with, and are discussed further in Chapter 22. However, there are some general guidelines which apply.

(a) When there are two parents, it is better if they can cooperate in the care of the children than having opposing views and practices.
(b) All members of a family should respect one another. The parents should respect the children's need to move towards independence. The children should respect the parents' need to live part of their lives separately from the children.
(c) Each family needs to decide what behaviour they find unacceptable and should be able to set limits to it.

Aims

The aims the therapists should have in mind obviously differ for parental and marital families. When the patient lives with two parents, the aims are:

(a) to encourage cooperation between mother and father so that they enhance each other's efforts rather than hindering them
(b) to maintain a balance of power between the parents so that they share responsibility for the patient equally

(c) to strengthen the boundaries between parents and children so that the schizophrenic offspring in particular can move towards independence

(d) to release the parents from full-time caring so that they can spend some time away from the patient enjoying each other's company.

These aims have to modified for single-parent households, in which it is usually the mother who is the carer. In this case a major aim is to develop or enhance links the carer has with people outside the household, in order to provide the emotional support they need and to create an alternative focus of interest to the patient.

In marital households the aims are:

(a) to maintain a balance of power between the partners (this may be difficult if the patient is very disabled by schizophrenia, but it must be recognised that the illness can be a source of power in itself – relatives may be frightened of violence, whether realistically or not, and on a more mundane level the patient can exploit the sick role to evade responsibility)

(b) to enhance the couple's enjoyment of the relationship; this is usually possible, unless it was a loveless marriage in the first place

(c) to help adjust the roles in the family so that the patient can find an area of competence that contributes to the well-being of the family; this might involve, for example, the wife going out to work while the husband looks after the children

(d) to ensure that the spouse gets some time off from care-giving.

Achieving the aims

This will be dealt with in detail throughout this manual, but it may be helpful to summarise the approaches here. They include the formation of alliances between the therapists and family members, modelling of cooperation and a balanced partnership by the co-therapists, setting tasks that bring the parents together and separate them from the children, exploring parental anxieties about separation from the children, giving each member an equal opportunity to speak, and changing where family members sit during a session.

Summary

Work with families has to take into account the norms for family structure and roles that exist in particular social and cultural groups. However, there are general principles for therapists to follow, such as the need for family members to respect each other and to cooperate in attempting to improve the quality of their lives.

7 Improving communication

The problems

Some families with a schizophrenic member communicate well, but others show disturbed patterns of communication which hinder useful work with the family. Often this is the result of high levels of emotional tension and trying to cope with numerous problems, both of which produce a stream of talk which is difficult to interrupt. We have found that high-EE relatives talk more than low-EE relatives, although the patients in the two types of family speak about the same amount. Many patients with schizophrenia are unable to assert themselves, and so get left out of conversations. In these families, members have often lost the ability to listen to one another, so that monologues become repetitive and are not modified by other people's responses.

A small minority of blood relatives express themselves in unusual ways which may impede communication. This characteristic is akin to schizophrenic thought disorder and shows itself by illogical jumps in the flow of speech or a peculiar use of words. In a multicultural society some family members may not speak English as their first language, and allowance needs to be made for lack of fluency. If the language problem is pronounced, a translator should be used, or better still a therapist who is fluent in the relevant language.

Establishing the ground rules

A good way of improving communication is to lay down a set of ground rules early on in the family meetings, and to help the family members to respect them. They are as follows.

(a) Only one person may speak at a time

This may appear obvious, but family members often speak over each other, sometimes carrying on parallel conversations with the two co-therapists. Therapists can introduce this rule by saying that it is impossible for them to listen to two people at once, and as they are keen to hear what everyone has to say, it is necessary for only one person to talk at a time. It can take many sessions for the family to settle down to a regular observance of this rule, and the therapists will often have to remind them of it repeatedly. This should be done firmly, but without criticising family members, for example "I'm sorry, we can only listen to one person at a time. Who is going to be first?"

Successful establishment of this rule means that family members have increased their self-control, both over speech and over the emotional pressure behind the speech. It also leads to them showing more respect for each other.

(b) Talk to the person, not about them

It is quite common for family members to talk about another person in the session, referring to them as 'he' or 'she', as though they were not present. It is often the patient who is referred to in the third person, particularly if they speak very little. It is surprisingly easy for therapists to slip into this practice unawares. It needs to be checked in family members whenever it occurs, because it makes the person referred to feel as though they were not really present. This is particularly problematic for schizophrenic patients, who often have a fragile sense of self. Moreover, it may be particularly uncomfortable for patients who are experiencing third-person auditory hallucinations.

The remedy is for the therapists to say something along the lines of: "We would like to establish a rule that if anyone wants to say something about a person in the room, they should speak directly to them". Family members will need frequent reminding of this rule. It can be helpful to say, "What you have just said is very important. Would you like to tell your husband directly."

Another advantage of direct communication is that it tones down the expression of negative emotions. It is much more difficult to say directly to someone "You're a very lazy person," than "He's a very lazy person".

(c) Speaking time should be shared out equally

It is quite common for one relative to take the lion's share of the conversation, to the exclusion of others, particularly the patient. The therapists need to explain that it is important to hear the views of each family member. They have to keep the more loquacious members in check and encourage the reticent ones. Stopping relatives in the middle of a sentence could be seen as rudeness. Therapists have to develop a style which is firm but tactful, for example "I know you have something important to say Mr Brown, but we would like to give your wife a chance to say something too, and we will come back to you later." The use of humour can sometimes sugar the pill.

Occasionally families cannot be kept in check this way and a more formal structure is required, for example giving each family member two minutes to talk.

The patient is usually the most disadvantaged in conversations and tends to get left out. This can be dealt with by giving the patient time in which to speak during which no other family member may interrupt. The patient may experience this as an uncomfortable pressure to contribute. In this case the therapists can reassure the patient that there is no need to speak at all during this time, but that everyone else will keep quiet and listen just in case they want to say something.

Listening skills

In addition to the ground rules, it is important for the therapists to improve family members' listening skills. This is partly achieved by preventing talking over and interrupting, but it can also be encouraged more actively. It can be helpful to point out to one family member that another is saying something important to them, and to ask them to listen carefully. When the speaker has finished talking, the listener can be asked to repeat what they said in their own words. This is a good check on how well or badly family members are communicating with each other.

Each person's point of view, however poorly expressed, should be valued by the therapists. This helps everyone to feel that they are contributing to the session. If someone is speaking in a muddled way, the therapists can say that they are not quite clear about the message and ask for clarification. If necessary the therapists can help a person towards a clearer expression of what they wish to convey.

Summary

Communication can be improved by establishing ground rules. Only one person should speak at a time. Family members should speak directly to each other. Everyone should get a fair share of speaking time. In addition family members often need encouragement to listen actively to each other.

8   Task setting

Setting a realistic list of goals

One of the most important tasks therapists have to undertake is to help families to deal with the many problems they might have. These problems might be a result of having to live with a member of the family suffering from a major mental illness or due to other factors in the family. Often intervention is in the form of problem solving. An essential ingredient of successful problem solving in therapy is to have an unambiguous list of goals. Problems defined vaguely or globally lead to vague or impossible solutions. Just as sometimes therapists ask a hostile relative to reframe and specify a global criticism – such as "He is so untidy" to "I would like him to clear up part of his bedroom..." – therapists have to ask the family to spell out goals in concrete terms that therapists and the family can work on. This might sound easier than it is in reality. However, it is an essential step in therapy. It might spread over several sessions and the list is constantly updated as therapy progresses.

Setting an agenda and prioritising

One of the characteristics of working with families with a schizophrenic member is the unpredictability the illness can bring. Hence therapy should be flexible, to accommodate any new or urgent problems. However, therapists should not be diverted to 'just putting out bushfires' session after session. A behavioural approach is particularly suited to this type of family work because it provides structure and continuity. The process is very much collaborative. At the beginning of each session, therapists should elicit any new problems the family might have had since the last session. These should be considered in conjunction with continuing problems that remain unresolved. Each family member should be given a chance to voice their problems and concerns. These in turn could be put on the agenda for negotiation and prioritising. It is often essential to focus on just one problem at a time. It is common for family members to divert the therapists from their focus on a single problem by raising equally pressing problems. This must be resisted politely but firmly with the explanation that progress can only be made by dealing with one problem at a time. It can also happen that as work on a problem is reaching a conclusion, irrelevant or diversionary topics are brought up, for example an offer to make tea for the therapists. As before, the therapists need to insist on maintaining the focus.

Clinical example

This illustrates how to set an agenda and focus on one problem at a time.

M. It's not only a drink problem. It's the money side of it, borrowing, borrowing, borrowing. Like today he has nothing left from social security to give me. And it is a terrible habit you have got into. If I suddenly disappeared, you wouldn't know what to do.

T1. I think part of the problem here is that there are a lot of problems. There are the drinking, budgeting, laundry and the weekend. So what does cause the most tension do you think, Peter [the patient]?

M. Well maybe not to Peter but it does to me dear. It has got to a point that I just go along with him. What else can I do?

T2. Well the purpose of coming here is to perhaps look at the problems and put them in sort of priority, some sort of order. Perhaps we should start with one. In dealing with one problem, we might make some impact on the others. Can we look at one and deal with one problem at a time?

The process of dealing with one thing at a time is not only realistic but also a good opportunity to 'role model' to the family how to solve problems. It would be advisable not to pick the most entrenched or difficult problem to deal with, at least initially, so that families can have some experience of success in therapy. All too often, their experience has been dominated by failure. It requires a lot of skill to persuade families to accept a less entrenched problem to focus on without thinking that their concerns and worries are being ignored.

Negotiating solutions and agreeing on homework

Problems should be spelled out precisely and in enough detail to enable a solution to be found. Global descriptions such as "He is so lazy" should be reframed as "He does not get up till noon". Once a problem is identified, each family member's views should then be explored. Patients' experiences related to the problems are particularly valuable. For example, the reason why a patient does not get up in the morning could be due to tiredness as a result of oversedation, or they simply have nothing to look forward to. The solution to this problem very much depends on the patient's experience.

Clinical example

This illustrates how the therapists should listen to everyone's view on the problem in order to understand.

T. Well it sounds to me like you are saying you don't want Peter to drink at the weekends and I am wondering Peter why you choose Saturday as your day to drink. Why don't you do it on a Thursday or a Monday, when you are not at your mother's house? You know she doesn't want you to drink?

P. Well I don't drink much on a Saturday. It's only four cans or something like that. It's usually because I have taken Sudafed in the day and it makes me hyper-tense in the evening. So if I take a drink it calms me down again. I think what I have got to do is stop taking the Sudafed and that will stop me drinking.

T. How about drinking at your mother's house? Could you do one or the other? Either you drink on Saturday and not go to your mother's house or you go to your mother and not drink.

M. The fact is that Peter will change after a drink. And I've seen that change many, many a time. But I am not having it any more. I'm not, no way. I have gone beyond that.

T. Do you find that a reasonable request?

P. Yes it's very reasonable.

T. Will you find that difficult?

P. Not because I change all that much. It's just that I find it difficult to talk to my mother when I have had a drink.

M. Maybe not, Peter, but you frighten me.

P. She can't have a conversation with me when I have had a drink because I am less inhibited. And she finds it difficult to get close to me when my inhibitions have gone. And plus the fact that there is a lot going on in my mind which could be potentially disturbing to her.

The therapists' next task is to encourage the family to express possible solutions to the problem, to look at the pros and cons of each solution, and to get the family to compromise and agree on a solution. When family members do not come up with desirable solutions spontaneously, the therapists' job is to move families skilfully to a low-EE solution.

Just as problems should be clearly defined, solutions should be operationalised in such a way that family members are clear about what each other's role is in carrying out the solution. Sometimes a relative's part is to do nothing, so that the patient can be given a chance to become more independent.

In negotiating the solution, therapists should also anticipate any blocks that might prevent it being effective. It could be that an overinvolved relative's anxiety is making the task too difficult or simply that the solution is too ambitious. It may be helpful to refer to the task as 'an experiment'. Failure can then be construed as a badly designed experiment for which the family is not to be blamed. Homework is important in therapy because it helps the family to generalise to the outside world what has been talked about in the session. The exact what, how, by whom, where, and when should be spelled out clearly, and in behavioural terms if possible. Sometimes it might be necessary for family members to write them down. To summarise, the steps are:

(a) specify in detail what the problem is
(b) get everyone's view on the problem, particularly the patient's
(c) elicit possible solutions
(d) look at the pros and cons of each possible solution
(e) compromise and agree on a desirable solution
(f) anticipate any obstacles
(g) spell out the exact what, how, by whom, where, and when
(h) assign the solution as an experiment as part of homework.

Clinical example
This is an example of how the therapists skilfully got the patient to agree on a solution that is workable and not too difficult for him.
T1. I was just wondering what can be done about your drinking or what you would like to do for the next weekend or for any weekend.
P. I want to stop it.
T1. I'm just wondering how practical it is.
P. I think it is pretty practical, I think I can manage it as long as I don't take the Sudafed.
T1. So if you don't take the Sudafed you wouldn't take the alcohol.
P. Yes.
T2. My own feelings about that is it's been a long-standing problem and it's not going to change overnight.
P. Yes.
T1. I am just wondering if we could try and work out something which is practical and possibly achievable before we meet again in terms of the first step.
P. Well can I make a promise to you that I'll not drink this week. I would feel very bad if I don't keep that promise. You're not forcing me into it, I'm volunteering it.
T1. No. But we want you to succeed at what we agree. There is no point in saying 'I will never drink', because that is very, very hard for someone with your problem. We need to go very slowly.
T2. It's very good of you to offer the promise. It sounds very laudable and very constructive. But it is a matter of pitching it at the point which is practical for you to achieve rather than promising so much and perhaps not achieving it. Perhaps it's best to promise less but make it achievable. I think our task is to break things down to the point where you can do something which is achievable.
P. But I think I realise now that it's not on if I drink on a Saturday. From my own point of view more than my mother's point of view. I

have a lot of feedback from elsewhere. I mean I talk to a psychologist and he said you are poisoning yourself every time you take a drink. I think that has sunk in pretty deeply and that is something that is playing on my mind. So I think it's feasible for me to say I won't have a drink on a Saturday, I think that is a reasonable goal at the moment.

Then the therapists anticipated problems which may prevent the patient from being successful in his task.

T1. So how could your mother help with this? Do you want to ask your mother if she could help anywhere?

P. Well I don't think she could. She could sit down and have a conversation with me. If I decided I wanted a drink, I could talk it through with her. But I don't think that would be a reasonable idea because then there is always the opportunity that I might be open for a drink if I could persuade her.

T2. And what about Saturday, how would you manage on Saturday? What's your routine normally?

P. Well if I promised it here and now, I don't think I am going to break my word.

T2. But I think when people have a problem with drink, you need to sort of say 'Well I'm going to do this and this to keep myself occupied'.

M. He hasn't done it every Saturday night.

P. I do some painting.

T2. But I think Peter, you need to have in your head what you are going to do to compensate. Have you any ideas? I mean you can't paint all day.

P. Not all day, but I can't paint in the evening. If I have a drink I can't paint at all so it's a waste of time.

The following shows how therapists engaged the mother to help.

T1. Have you any ideas [to mother]?

M. Look at it this way Peter. When you haven't spent all this money on beer, there is nothing to stop us going to the theatre. That's where we used to go.

T2. That would be nice.

M. As long as you pay your share. I can't afford it for the two. But you're spending it on something constructive and not going to have the beer. If I've got to drink all those beers, it would be enough to make my head ache.

T2. I think it is important to praise Peter. He is doing well and likes going to the theatre which you might enjoy together.

P. Yeah.

T1. So do you want to plan that in now as part of this package, that Peter would not drink on Saturday and do some painting? What is planned in as well is the theatre trip on Saturday.

Checking up on homework

It is extremely frustrating for families to be given homework and for therapists not even to bother to find out how it has gone in the next session. Finding out about homework from the last session should always be on the agenda if homework has been agreed on. Enough time should be allocated to go through homework thoroughly. If the agreed solution has been successful, the therapists should positively reinforce the family members involved. Other family members should be encouraged to praise and value any change, no matter how small it is. This is important, as it provides a model for recognising that small changes are the aim and must not be devalued. Family members then should be encouraged to try the solution again and to practise it whenever the opportunity arises. They should also be encouraged to generalise the principle or the solution to other problems.

Clinical example

This illustrates how therapists encourage relatives to praise and value any small changes.

T1. Just wondering how things have been since two weeks ago. The agreement was for John to look after his own washing. We were talking about you doing less for John as a way of possibly satisfying both views on your responsibilities. We agreed that John would do more, to reduce what you were doing for him.

M. I don't think it's materialised yet, not at the moment. I think John's trying to bring less washing to me but he didn't do any last week, because of the worry I suppose. It's a bit peculiar what I'm going to say. But whatever he does in the day centre, the sheets and shirts are very screwed up. It's an awful job to iron them and get them back to normal again. I have a machine which I can do myself and they come out reasonably for ironing. Here they come out sort of really screwed up and its hard work to iron them. So I don't know which is the better of two evils.

T2. How do you feel John?

P. Well I didn't really feel like coming in on the Wednesday. I have very little washing because I got most of it done the previous week. I took a few things around to my mother's on Friday. But tomorrow I shall be able to do it again.

T2. You started to make an effort.

M. Yes he makes an effort to do towels and things like that. But learn to put them straight John and you don't get all that bundled up, if you know what I mean.

T1. So the first step appears to be that John attempts to do the washing. That's the first step.

M. Yes he's trying.

T2. And then you know that you're trying to improve.

T1. How are the results to you John, were they acceptable to you?

P. Not really because I was shirking.

T1. Shirking?

P. Yes. I wasn't really putting a great effort into it last week. I felt down last week so that had something to do with it. But I should imagine this week that I will be able to do it, perhaps tomorrow. I think tomorrow.

M. Well its good to be occupied. That's good – it helps me a bit.

Sometimes, despite the ingenuity and preparations of the therapists and the family, the solution may not work. This is part of therapy, and therapists should not feel angry or become despondent about the family. Therapists should find out exactly what happened and why nothing was attempted if that was the case. Sometimes an unsuccessful intervention can be just as useful in the long run, as it can elucidate much about the family and its members. On no account should therapists blame or become angry with the family. Therapists accept responsibility for failure. "The task was set too soon or was too difficult," "The experiment was poorly designed," or "The family is not ready for it yet" are some of the good ways for therapists to avoid blaming the family. Therapists should 'role model' how to deal with failures, which are part of life. The problem should be looked at again or a new problem chosen. Individual family member's views should be listened to and a new solution should be agreed upon, taking into account the obstacles causing the failure. This starts the whole process over again.

Summary

Agreeing on a list of goals, setting an agenda, prioritising, agreeing on solutions, and homework assignment is very much a collaborative process. Each family member's views and feelings should be elicited in turn. They should be listened to carefully and respected. The therapy process is just as important as the content. It is particularly therapeutic to make sure the patient's views are listened to, no matter how passive or withdrawn the patient might be. This might be the only opportunity for the family to listen to each other's views with a constructive aim. Overinvolved relatives who might have a tendency to think they know the patient's views or feelings without asking the patient are shown that it is important to ask and listen to the patient. This can help foster respect for patients as individuals with their own thoughts and feelings. A lot of skill is required, as well as a clear idea of goals and techniques.

9 Dealing with emotional upset: general issues

The variety of emotional responses

We know that living with schizophrenia gives rise to a wide variety of emotional responses. Families may deny there is a problem, particularly at the beginning of an illness. They may try hard to say that all difficulties are in the past and that problems will not recur. They may have many negative emotions; relatives are likely to feel angry, they may sometimes be rejecting and wish the patient were not living with them, or that they could leave.

Relatives who are parents are almost certain to feel guilty and in some way to blame for the problems. They will often respond by sacrificing their own time and energy, offering care and protection and trying to make things better. Some relatives may take this to extremes and attempt to do everything, to take over all the roles and treat the patient as a child again, not as an autonomous adult. In the short term, while the illness is florid, this can be a helpful reaction. In the long term, it impedes recovery because a patient has nothing to gain by an inappropriate, childish, sick role in the family, and is likely both to lose skills and to become overdemanding of the care needed.

Another emotion experienced is feelings of loss. There are two kinds of loss that may have to be faced. One is almost like a bereavement, and is the loss of the person that existed before the illness (see epigraph on p. v): the familiar relative seems to have been replaced by a stranger. The other is a loss of expectation and ambitions: hopes of achievement, career, and autonomy may have to be modified. Both losses may include an inability to accept how the patient is now. Patients themselves may well have had to cope with loss of their old self, of skills, a job, a role in the community. These losses are often accompanied by reduced confidence and a worry about trying new things. Both relatives and patient may be frightened of change in case the illness returns, and may not be sure how much they can cope with it.

Sometimes there is overt depression in the family. The patient may become depressed by the losses and difficulties in rebuilding life; relatives may become depressed by the burden of care, isolation, and feeling that no one understands. In elderly carers there is an inevitable worry about the future: "Who will look after the patient when I am gone?" There may be general anxiety and confusion about what has happened and what the future will hold.

Normalising emotional responses

The important thing to emphasise to the family during a session is the *normality* of any of these emotions, especially the negative ones. The feelings that families have, however intense, are typical of any family having to face the change and upset that can accompany living with schizophrenia. They may even be helpful in forcing family members to acknowledge that there are problems and thus to engage in treatment because they need some help.

Clinical example
This is an example of the therapist normalising the relative's feeling of upset at the patient's disturbed behaviour.
M. Sometimes he comes to you and says, "I want to do this." I say, "Oh yes, of course, why not." Then he goes away and comes back and says, "No, I change my mind."
F. Yes, he changes his mind quick. So we can't ask him to go on holiday. He says "Yes" and then says, "No, I don't want to go." We want to take him on holiday, but when he does things like that, we worry. We spend money and then he tells you 'no'.
T. All that changing his mind, that's a very common problem. It's what relatives often experience with people with schizophrenia.

Therapists must allow relatives to admit to these feelings and not be taken aback or feel shocked by them. Negative emotions exist and should be acknowledged and listened to. However, what must also be done is to make sure that during a session, negative feelings are not used as a way of attacking other family members. Overtly hostile, critical, or intrusive statements need to be picked up by therapists and prevented from causing argument and upset.

One of the major aims of the intervention is to reduce relatives' expression of criticism. Criticism is fuelled by anger with the patient, which often stems from a misunderstanding of the patient's behaviour. We have found that the majority (70%) of critical comments are about the negative symptoms of schizophrenia. Relatives do not appreciate that these are part of the illness. Instead, they view them as being under the patient's control and consequently blame the patient for behaving badly. Part of the education programme is aimed at changing the critical relative's understanding of negative symptoms. Other components, particularly the problem-solving approach, are intended to help the patient overcome the negative symptoms. In the long term, these techniques are effective in softening relatives' critical attitudes. However, when criticism is expressed during a session, therapists should take action to moderate its negative effect. The way to do this is called *positive reframing*.

Positive reframing

This is an important technique that therapists need to become familiar with and be able to practise as part of their training. It channels negative emotion so that it can be used constructively during a family session.

Positive reframing is a way of getting underneath negative emotion, and pointing out that there is a positive reason for the intensity of the feeling. If relatives were not concerned and did not care, they would not be in a session trying to sort things out. We have always found it possible to find a positive aspect of even the most hostile or negative statement, and this is the requirement for therapists.

For instance, rejecting remarks, such as "I can't stand living with you" can be reframed as the relative feeling so upset by the illness and what it does that they wish that things were different. "I can't let you look after yourself" can be reframed as a worry that the person will not manage and might come to harm. "What will happen when I'm not here to look after you?" is a realistic worry about the future that both relative and patient need to consider. It may be possible to aim at increasing coping skills so that the patient will be less vulnerable, and more independent. Other strategies include not allowing family members to talk about someone else during a session. As discussed previously, making it a rule that relatives talk directly to each other means it is less easy to be overtly hostile, and is likely to defuse the feelings.

Seeing family members separately

If negative feelings are prominent in a session it may be necessary to see parts of the family separately for a while, in order to allow and acknowledge the intensity of emotional upset. Separate sessions for parts of the family can enforce generational boundaries, cement marital alliances, and allow therapists to listen to emotional issues without the worry that it will upset a patient or other family members. It may also be a useful way to engage families who feel that no one has previously listened to them or taken their problems seriously. However, even if some sessions are with separate family members it can be helpful to bring the family back together for the last few minutes of a session and mention the issues that each part brought up, if they involve the rest of the family. Unless the aim of a session is to separate hostile or intractable relatives (which will only happen in extreme cases) then acknowledging and looking at areas of mutual concern is the beginning of the therapeutic process.

If it is available, a relatives' group can be a good way of dealing with emotional issues. All the relatives will have felt the intensity of the feelings, the normality of such emotions can be demonstrated, feelings can be ventilated without fear of upsetting the patient, and families who have felt upset but have coped with it can discuss how this was done.

Very occasionally, if therapists are really stuck, role play can be used in a family or relatives' group. This is a powerful technique and has to be used with safeguards. Putting a critical or hostile parent into the role of the patient and asking the patient to demonstrate a relative's viewpoint forces a relative to empathise with the patient's experiences. We have used this technique, but relatives and patient must be 'de-roled', therapists must take control and do it for a short time only, and any feelings and worries must be discussed carefully afterwards.

Summary

Emotional responses in families include guilt, loss, anger and depression. Therapists must be able to cope with these and help to normalise them. Many of the negative emotions fuel criticism by family members. Overtly negative statements during family sessions should be interrupted, and therapists need to reframe them positively.

10 How families affect professionals

The spread of conflict

There are strong emotional tensions in high-EE families. It is easy for them to be transmitted to the therapists and mirrored by them. If there are two parents, it is common for there to be conflict between them about how to tackle the problems raised by the patient. A frequent pattern is for the mother to be overinvolved and the father to be critical. The mother then criticises the father for being too hard, while he criticises her for being too soft.

Clinical example
This illustrates contrasting attitudes by two parents which can lead to conflict.
F.   You see we take two different approaches. See, she's got a very soft approach. She always has had. Well, I mean, mothers do, don't they? I think really Paul has been, I should say, a mother's boy. And he plays on it a little bit sometimes. But I've been the other way. I don't believe in molly-coddling. I say she's too soft and she says I'm too hard.

Conflict can also develop between a single parent and a patient, and, in marital homes, between the patient and spouse. The warring family members do their best to win one or other of the therapists over to their side. It can happen that one therapist is more sympathetic to one of the sparring partners, while the co-therapist leans towards the other. This can readily lead to a split between the therapists which will impair their working relationship. Therapists should always be on the look-out for the development of tensions with their working partners. When they occur, the first thing to do is to examine how they might reflect tensions between family members. Once the source of them is identified, they can be dealt with effectively.

Sometimes conflict within the family can spread beyond the co-therapists to the wider clinical team. The situation is ripe for this to happen when there are already divisions within the team, for example between health and social services staff, or between hospital and community staff. It is of the highest importance to preserve good working relationships within the whole group of staff involved with the family, or they will be unable to offer effective help. Regular communication within the team about the therapeutic activities with the family can help to prevent conflict. Once it is apparent, however, it is essential to hold a meeting of all the staff concerned, to locate the source of the conflict. While this may sometimes stem from interprofessional rivalries and tension, such conflict can originate from the family, and this source should always be considered.

Doom and gloom

At some stage in their life with a schizophrenic person, most relatives become overwhelmed by a sense of hopelessness and despair. It seems to them that, despite their best efforts and the help of professionals, the patient is making no progress.

Clinical example
This is an example of the patient communicating hopelessness to the relative, who then expresses it to the therapist.
M. I don't think John is getting any better. He's getting a lot worse. I'm very worried. You know you can't help him. He's very depressed. He's always contemplating suicide.

They are usually quite open in communicating these painful experiences to the therapists, who can easily become equally overwhelmed by them and come to believe that there really is no hope and nothing that will help.

It is important for the therapists to bring these feelings to their support group. Their peers need to remind them that these feelings come from the family, rather than originating in themselves, and that there is always something that can be done, however small, that might lead to an improvement. Once it is clear that the source is the family, the group can begin to 'brain-storm' the problems. The group acts as a valuable resource for generating new ideas and ways of tackling problems when the therapists get stuck. With the support of their group behind them, therapists can sustain families through periods of hopelessness.

Guilt and anger

Other responses shown by relatives to lack of progress by the patient are guilt and anger. Guilty relatives tend to contact a large variety of professionals and services, attempting to get them all to act on the patient's behalf. They are sometimes successful in engaging a variety of people, who get involved because they begin to feel guilty that they are not doing enough for the patient. In this respect they mirror the guilt of the relative. The usual result is a number of professionals working at cross purposes, which is not helpful for the patient or the family. It is preferable for the therapist to help relatives understand their sense of guilt and to emphasise that they are doing the best possible for the patient by working together with the therapists. Attendance at a relatives' group can also reduce feelings of guilt when relatives realise that they are not struggling in isolation with unique problems, but share much in common with others.

Angry relatives tend to blame the staff and the services for the patient's slow progress. By doing so, they often alienate the staff and actually receive a worse service than if they had not complained. Such relatives need help from the therapists to appreciate why they are angry and to lower their expectations for the patient. They may also need assistance in improving their relationship with other members of staff, which is likely to involve the therapists acting as advocates on behalf of the family.

Summary

Strong emotions originating in the family are communicated to the therapists and the other members of staff and may impede the process of working with the family. In general, if therapists begin to have strong feelings about the family, such as guilt, anger or hopelessness, it is important to recognise that they are likely to be mirroring emotions in the family and to discuss them with the co-therapist and with the support group. Once their origin is recognised, the therapists will find it much easier to deal with them and to continue with useful work.

11 Leaving

Family work is time limited and has to come to a halt at some point. Sessions are usually held every fortnight for the first six to nine months and then reduced to once a month. Some families have sorted out their main problems by nine months while others need regular sessions for as long as three years. Therapists may decide that the time has come to leave the family, or a therapist may have to leave for professional reasons. Either way, the family needs plenty of warning (at least one month and preferably more) of the leaving date to prepare themselves and to work through the feelings aroused.

Establishing a lifeline

If the therapist is leaving while work remains to be done, a replacement therapist may be found, and should be introduced to the family before the familiar therapist leaves. For families with obviously long-term problems, it is advisable to assign a more senior therapist to provide greater continuity, to avoid the inevitable disruptions that accompany leaving. If the therapists have come to the end of their work, they need to leave the family with a telephone number to contact them or some other appropriate professional. This acts as a lifeline which, from our experience, families do not abuse, but use when they have genuine need. The therapists need to warn the families that there may be a recurrence of old problems or the appearance of new ones, and to tell them that they should not be surprised by this, because it is in the nature of schizophrenia. Relatives may find themselves able to cope with these problems themselves, but if not they should telephone.

During discussions about the process of leaving, the family may express feelings of anger and loss about being deserted. They may feel that since they will be caring for the patient for many years to come, they will continue to need the support of the therapists. Establishing the lifeline of a contact number is one way of dealing with this. However, throughout the sessions the aim is to help the family to identify their strengths and to gain confidence that they have the resources to deal with their problems. Thus from the very beginning the therapists are working towards the goal of the family's independence from them.

The therapists may experience feelings of guilt and responsibility themselves at leaving families. These should be explored in the therapists' support group, which is an essential component in any service.

Reviewing the family work

As the sessions draw to a close it is natural for the family and the therapists to review what changes have occurred. The therapists will usually be able to identify positive changes in relatives' attitudes and behaviour towards the patients and in the patient's level of activity. However, family members may find it difficult to acknowledge the changes. Any alteration in the way they relate to each other can be seen as threatening, involving a leap into the unknown. The therapists may have to be content with their own recognition of the positive effects of their work with the family, without the additional satisfaction of the family's gratitude. Under no circumstances should they attempt to press the family to admit that change has taken place.

Rarely, one or more members of the family express the wish to stop the sessions before the therapists consider it is appropriate. This requires negotiation, particularly if family members disagree about it. However, it may lead to a premature ending of sessions. As above, the therapists should not attempt to prove to the family the value of their work together, as this will lead to confrontation and unproductive argument. The therapists have to accept that the family no longer want them to visit their home. Ways of responding to this are discussed in the final section of Chapter 23.

Summary

Families need plenty of warning of the therapists' intention to stop the sessions. Therapists should leave the family with a telephone number by which they can be contacted. Changes that have occurred during the family work should be reviewed, but it may be difficult for family members to acknowledge them. Therapists are advised not to press this issue.

12 Anger, conflict, rejection

Despite what has been said earlier about dealing with emotional issues in general, family members will get angry with each other. Some families do not know how to discuss anything without having an argument. Sometimes just sitting in a room together will spark conflict in a family that has avoided issues or each other. Sometimes views are held so strongly, or feelings are so intense, that family members say hurtful and rejecting things to each other. At times these feelings may lead to violence – either verbal abuse such as shouting, or physical abuse. Although it is unusual for the latter to happen during sessions, it can be part of the family interaction pattern. One of the commonest examples of this is when an overinvolved parent, usually a mother, is unable to put any limits on the behaviour of their adult son or daughter, who then can become overly demanding and threatening in the childish, sick role they occupy.

Defusing anger

Therapists must feel confident that they can defuse anger and potential or actual violence. The social constraints of the family meeting may help, as the expression of even very strong feelings may be tempered by having two non-family members as witnesses. Rejecting remarks can be defused by positively reframing them (see p. 34). Arguments and conflict can be defused by ensuring that each family member is listened to. If necessary the rules of turn-taking and listening can be formalised, by giving each family member, say, two minutes in which to make their views known. The other rules of family meetings, such as not allowing members to talk *about* each other in the third person (he/she is very difficult) but only to talk directly in the second person (you are difficult) will help family members themselves to defuse statements.

Another method of defusing angry statements is to ensure that individuals specify what it is that they are so cross about. Therapists must move statements from the general (you are so lazy) to behaviour (I want you to get up in the morning). Once behaviour has been specified, therapists and the family have a problem to work on; something which potentially can be modified.

Clinical example

This illustrates the therapist asking the patient to focus on a specific problem instead of expressing general anger.

P.   I think it is outrageous. I mean somehow she's running. I know she's been in a car crash and she hasn't got much in her head, but really, just out of common decency she wouldn't go out with somebody like that.

T.   It would help you, Colin, if we looked at what the problem's about, and just take it in turn to say what the problem is, so we can move towards a resolution.

Keeping control

Therapists should make sure that they keep control of the family if anger or potential violence is in evidence. Most families respond to clear and firm reminders of why they are meeting (to try to help with the problems) and of the rules outlined in Chapter 7. However, if repetitive argument develops, or conflict seems to be escalating, it is important that therapists intervene. This requires skill and confidence, but it is a way of containing the fear that anger will generate, and of making the family feel safe.

Clinical example

This is an example of the therapist intervening to prevent an angry exchange escalating further.

M.   It's been going on for a long time about the shirts. I say, "Full stop! Don't bring anything home at all. Get on with it."

P.   Bird brain, don't talk to me like that, and talk past me. You're a fool.

T.   David, it doesn't help very much if you make derogatory comments. If there's something that's upsetting you, we're here to try and help.

Some families may use the opportunity of therapists visiting to enact their arguments, because of the safety that visitors imply. Therapists should make it clear that conflict and arguments are not tolerated and do not form part of a constructive family session. It can help to reframe the anger itself. This is done by talking about the strength of feeling that family members obviously have, and how much it shows that they care about how difficult and upsetting things may be at present. This is a way of using the negative emotion constructively, and helping the family to channel their strong feelings into making changes, rather than being destructive and feeling hopeless about the future.

Clinical example

This is an example of the therapist blocking the patient's criticism of his mother, reframing it positively, and encouraging the patient to be constructive.

P. The way she carries on with Edward, it's all wrong. It's not right at all. I'm saying that my mother's not strong enough to know that people can control her, quite easily control her, control her mind, but she's not strong enough to know that.

T. It feels as if you're taking a lot of responsibility for what your mother does or for your mother's life in terms of who she chooses. It seems that you're concerned about your mother's way of life.

P. Well it is half concern for my mother, but the other half is things are rotten and going. . . [therapist interrupts].

T. I was wondering whether you could say something different to your mother. If it's about concern, whether you can actually say what the concerns are about.

If, in extreme cases, families do not respond to any of the above, or if, for whatever reason, they stop listening to the therapists and shout or attack each other, then the therapists need to separate them, and each therapist should see part of the family system. Sometimes family members arrive at a meeting already angry and upset, and this can make it difficult for therapists to start a constructive session. If family members are immediately seen separately, this enables both sides to calm down, and the therapists to have a chance to assess the problems and get difficulties reframed. If parts of the family are seen in this way it is still important to regroup for the last few minutes so that both sides can hear what has been discussed.

Model positive negotiation

Therapists must be able to deal with conflicts between themselves and negotiate differences in a positive way. As described in Chapter 4, modelling a constructive resolution to genuine differences of opinion may be the only example a family is exposed to of how this can be done. Because of the role modelling they provide, therapists must also make sure that they do not 'take sides' with family members (unless in a planned way as an advocate), as this will leave others feeling neglected and misunderstood. Therapists need also to be aware that their own behaviour, when under pressure or when an argument starts, is important. Therapists should not shout back, should not show irritation or anger, and should not make critical or rejecting remarks themselves, even if provoked. Remaining calm, talking in an even tone, not being visibly shocked or upset by a family's behaviour, and taking firm preventive action if necessary, are important ways of ensuring safety and control.

If therapists do encounter violence and hostility between family members, it will help to remember that the family will almost certainly have behaved in a much more extreme way at other times. Therapists are unlikely to elicit behaviour that is not already part of an established pattern. Even the most rejecting and angry remarks or actions will usually have been said or done many times previously; when they are demonstrated, therapists have an opportunity to allow the family to look at and begin to modify them.

Look at the positive aspects

Once conflict or the threat of physical harm has been defused, therapists should aim to start looking at the problems that they illustrate. Therapists should try to move the family away from negative escalation and begin to build in again positive aspects which family members have lost. We have found that even in very angry relationships, the fact that there *is* a relationship means that there is a positive side. Family members are likely still to care for each other and to want things to improve. Therapists can ask each family member to say something positive, to ask what they *do* like about each other. Occasionally family members fall silent at this point. Therapists can offer some suggestions about positive things that they have noticed. It may be that behaviour in the past has been positive but has not been tried recently. Positive behaviour can be neglected or taken for granted even in relationships not characterised by conflict; it needs to be elicited, valued, listened to, and therapists must help family members to do this for each other. If necessary, check that positive comments have been heard and registered – ask a family member to repeat what has just been said about them.

Limit setting

If limit setting is a problem, the steps involved need to be gone through in detail. In a family unable to manage this, members need permission to set limits, and then a great deal of help both to set reasonable limits (agreed with the other person, not imposed) and then to try them out consistently. This is discussed in detail in Chapter 13.

Unpacking a violent incident

Finally, if actual violence has occurred, either before or within a session, the incident needs to be looked at in a further session in order to try to prevent it recurring. Some days after a violent event, when both sides are calm, therapists should go through the incident in detail. Both sides should give their version of events and should be listened to. Feelings that the violence caused should be elicited. Each side should tell the other what it felt like. It can be easy otherwise for one or both sides to pretend that the event was not that important. This loses the opportunity to feed back realistically how hurtful and upsetting it was (to be the victim) and how angry and upsetting it was (to be the perpetrator). Any triggering incidents should be clearly identified in order either to modify or to avoid them in future. Often a pattern will be obvious which can then be interrupted.

Prevention

In order to try to prevent violence recurring, the family should try to rehearse ways of coping if a similar situation should arise. The perpetrator may be able to give warning of feeling angry (and possibly violent). Anger and conflict may be part of an impending relapse, and help can then be organised for this. Simple strategies such as avoidance or calming down can be used. The angry person can be encouraged to withdraw to their room or go out for a walk for a while. How to call in help if things start to get out of control should also be discussed. Therapists should stress the need for family members to be able to feel safe. If necessary it may be possible to call in the care team, the general practitioner, or in extreme instances the police. Discussing these difficult options when everyone is calm is likely to help prevent dangerous outcomes in the future.

Summary

Anger and violence are frightening, but may form part of family interactions. Therapists need to defuse potentially escalating negative interchanges. If necessary they should separate family members and see them separately. Therapists themselves must model positive interaction and settle differences by negotiation – they must not join in with family conflict. Once defused, negative patterns should be replaced by positive ones; often the family will need considerable help to do this. If violence has occurred, it needs to be discussed calmly afterwards, and strategies for future prevention rehearsed.

13 Dealing with overinvolvement

General considerations

It is important to recognise that overinvolvement usually has a much longer history than criticism, and consequently the time over which change can be achieved is also longer – years rather than months. It is not uncommon for the relative to describe overinvolved attitudes developing in the patient's childhood, sometimes in response to a serious physical illness in the child, to delayed milestones, or to some other deviation from normal development.

A crucial aspect of an overinvolved relationship is its symmetry. The relative and patient are equally dependent on each other, and equally anxious about each other's welfare. The relative worries about how the patient would manage without them, and the patient shares the same anxiety owing to the lack of confidence that results from being overprotected.

Clinical example
This illustrates a patient's anxieties about the health of her overprotective mother.

M. I get it at night. I get woken up in the night. I'm having a lovely sleep and I get woken up. "Are you alright mummy? Oh, I thought you was dead."

It is necessary to deal with the anxieties of both partners in order to weaken the bond between them. Attempts to achieve separation rapidly and forcibly without dealing with the underlying emotional bonds often have the reverse effect, of pushing the partners closer together. One or other of them will almost invariably sabotage the arrangements made.

Overinvolvement usually develops in a parent's relationship with a son or daughter. Only occasionally do we see it in other relationships, such as between spouses. The point of trying to effect change in order to separate the overinvolved pair is that such a relationship not only overburdens the relative, but also hinders a patient's recovery by preventing the practice of skills such as self-care. We work towards separation in order to allow the normal process of adult individuation to occur in the son or daughter, and also to enable the patient to begin to contribute again within the family, thus alleviating guilt and feelings of uselessness.

In the case of spouses, the aim is normally to encourage some recovery of the adult role in the family, even if this has been affected by the illness; for example a patient who is a spouse may not be able to manage a paid job, but could still contribute by doing work around the house.

It is also important to aim for separation and independence in cases where the parent and son or daughter have become so locked together that the patient's demands cannot be refused. If the demands escalate, this situation can easily lead to resentment and violence, and can be dangerous. These issues are discussed in Chapter 12.

Relative's guilt

The emotion most often found to underlie overinvolved behaviour is guilt. Relatives may feel personally responsible for the patient falling ill and dedicate themselves to making everything come right for the patient. Thus they will attempt to do everything for the patient, which has the effect of undermining the patient's confidence and increasing dependence on the relative.

Clinical example
This illustrates a relative's sense of guilt at separating from the patient for a brief period to attend to her own needs.
W. When I have left and been gone for a whole week, I'm worried sick in case he's overdone the pills or he's gone out and got himself drunk, and I'm saying, "What if he's in the gutter somewhere?" It's my fault, you know. You get no peace. You can't go to the ends of the earth because they're here, and there's no way you can shut them out.

The relative's sense of guilt can be lessened by repeated assurance that relatives cannot cause schizophrenia. It can also be diminished as a result of meeting others at a relatives' group. However, some relatives may find it a relief to talk about their guilty feelings one-to-one with the therapist.

Finding a lever

If the overinvolved relative and the patient are apparently satisfied with their relationship and there is no other adult in the household, it can be difficult for the therapists to find a lever to effect change. If another adult is present in the household they may resent the closeness between the overinvolved couple, in which case they can be recruited as an ally by the therapists. Otherwise, a strategy we find useful with a single overinvolved parent is to draw their attention to the 'when I am gone' scenario. This is a common concern of elderly parents of schizophrenic adults who cannot see any prospect of another person or professional providing the same level of care after their death.

Clinical example
This is an example of a father presenting the 'when I am gone' scenario to the patient.
F.   I tell him every time I get a chance. I say, "Do something because later on if we die, I don't know who will look after you. While we live it's alright, but tomorrow you don't know."

The parent is asked to imagine what things will be like in, say, one year, five years, and 15 years (the collapsed-time technique). This then becomes an argument for increasing patients' independence and ability to care for themselves. In other families, patients may express discontent with the restriction on their freedom and the intrusion into their privacy. On the other hand, parents may resent the burden and the lack of privacy that the patient's dependence creates. Discontent in either partner provides an opening for the therapists to begin work.

Exploring anxieties about separation

In order to persuade the patient and relative to begin the process of separation, it is necessary first to explore the relatives' anxieties about what might happen if they relaxed their vigilance. They often protest that if they were to go out and leave the patient, the patient might damage the home or themselves. These fears of the worst outcome need to be discussed with the relative and the patient and their likelihood weighed up. They almost always turn out to be exaggerated.

Clinical example
This illustrates a mother's anxieties about allowing the patient to perform an age-appropriate activity.
M.   I don't like Cheryl going to the hospital by bus because she has to cross the road at the other end. At this end I can take her across the road myself.
T.   But isn't there a traffic light by the hospital?
M.   Yes, but she's always in another world. You can't trust her to look out for herself.
T.   Cheryl, is there a light to tell you when to cross, you know, with a green man on it?
P.   I think so.

T. Do you think you could use the light to help you cross safely?

P. I think so.

This next example is of the therapist encouraging a mother to on holiday and exploring her anxieties about leaving the patient.

T. It sounds like you went away to friends before for weekends and things.

M. Yes, but since he's been ill, I don't.

T. I wondered about that. Why's that?

M. Probably just me. Just in case anything happens and they need me.

T. What is your worst fear about what might happen while you're away?

M. Er, just in case he got worse or, all sorts of things can happen, you know. All sorts of silly things, or in a sense they're not silly, are they? When you hear all these things that happen.

T. But has anything like that ever happened that has made you worry?

M. No, no, but it's within yourself and, oh, I don't know. I suppose sooner or later when you're a mother, you. . . I suppose you. . .

T. I suppose there is always a possibility of those things happening. I mean, maybe you can't say they're not going to happen. But I suppose the likelihood is that they probably won't, and in a sense you do have to get on and live your life, and that's important.

It can also be useful to get the relative to face the impossibility of maintaining constant vigilance – they have to sleep at some time. We then negotiate with the relative to leave the patient alone on a trial basis for a short time, say half an hour. Of course, the therapists cannot guarantee that nothing disastrous will happen, but they can reassure the relative that the chances are very small indeed, and that it is a risk worth taking. The first small step is usually the most difficult, and once achieved leads to more rapid progress.

In helping the parent to choose an activity that will take them out of the home, there are a number of factors to consider. If there is a spouse in the household, the two parents should be encouraged to go out together. Often the marriage has suffered because of the overinvolved parent's dedication to the patient and through conflict over the management of daily difficulties. The parents need to rediscover a sense of pleasure in each other's company and to experience some relief from the burden of constantly caring for the patient. They often seem to need the therapists' permission to relax and enjoy themselves. We formulate the permission as follows: "You have worked so hard to look after the patient that you have earned a rest". Relatives usually experience a considerable easing of the burden of responsibility when they find that they can leave the patient even for a short while without a tragedy occurring.

Some relatives have no partner, in which case the therapists encourage the relative to resuscitate their contacts with friends and relations outside the home. Often they have withdrawn from their social networks through shame and embarrassment, and have thereby lost a valuable source of emotional support.

Clinical example

This is an example of the therapist beginning to explore the possibility of a mother using her social network.

T.   Do you have any friends around here that are supportive for you, Sandra? Have you got any good friends around?
M.   What do you mean supportive?
T.   Well, someone that will listen to you, that will support you in the same way that you support your niece and your son.
M.   Well, yes, I suppose so.

Relatives may also need encouragement to resume leisure interests they had previously, or even to return to work if they have given this up in order to look after the patient.

Overinvolved parents often have an additional fear of losing their relationship with the son or daughter once separation begins. We normalise this anxiety by pointing out that all children have to achieve psychological separation from their parents, although schizophrenia delays the process. Furthermore once separation has been negotiated, the two partners have the opportunity to establish a new, more adult relationship. The parent may still need to come to terms with losing their child and can be helped with this by other parents in the relatives' group who have been through this process and appreciate the eventual advantages.

Limit setting

One aspect of overinvolvement, excessive self-sacrifice, can be shown by the relative allowing the patient's disturbed behaviour to encroach too much on their own life. Alternatively they may try to meet every demand the patient makes on them, however unreasonable, in the same way that some parents are overindulgent to their children. This behaviour stems from the relative's sense of guilt (see p. 47).

In addition, relatives should be encouraged to respect their own needs and sense of comfort. This will inevitably involve them setting limits on the patient's behaviour and demands. On the other hand, patients should be given the opportunity to state what limits they would want the relative to observe with respect to overprotection and intrusiveness into their lives. In order to establish both these sets of limits it is necessary to negotiate an agreement between the patient and relative. This needs to be based on mutual respect and should not be operated punitively: some relatives vacillate between no limits and unreasonable demands. Both partners to the agreement have to be prepared to maintain the limits firmly and consistently and not give in to persuasion, demands, or threats. These can be difficult for relatives to withstand, particularly if they have a strong sense of guilt concerning the patient. If the relative appears incapable of maintaining firm limits, it is an indication for further exploration of their guilty feelings. Relatives often benefit from permission from the therapists to establish limits. An example of limit-setting by a relative is provided by the wife who told her husband she realised he could not help talking aloud to the voices, but that he would have to do it in another room. An example of limit-setting by a patient is that of a son who established with his mother that she could visit his flat only once a week instead of three times to check on his tidiness.

Some families are helped by formulating the limit as a contract which both sides agree to and write down.

Achieving independence

While the parent is gradually letting go, patients need to build up confidence in their ability to look after themselves. The therapists seek agreement between family members on small achievable tasks for the patient to tackle. These have to be relatively undemanding at first to minimise the possibility of failure. Examples might be emptying the rubbish bin or washing underclothes once a week. It is a good plan to start with activities directed at self-care or care of the patient's bedroom, since these are often areas of intrusive concern by the overinvolved parent. A common response by the parent to the setting of such a task is to say that the patient does not do the job properly and it is better to take over.

Clinical example
This is an example of a wife with high standards finding it hard to tolerate the patient's less efficient ways of doing things.
T. Michael, I was wondering if Polly asked you to do a task and she offered to help you, to work together with you to do it, would you feel more able to do the task?
P. Yes.
T. Have you ever told her this?
P. No. Er, let's think now. Polly is like a back-seat driver. She has to have it done her way. That way doesn't suit me, so I down tools, you know. I down tools.
T. I think it's very difficult when you've both got different standards for doing things. That must be difficult for you, Polly, particularly as you like things done to perfection.
W. I probably set myself high standards, expecting them from everybody else too.
T. Yes.
W. That's about right, isn't it? I'm fussy.

The therapists need to work towards lowering relatives' expectations for patients' performance, emphasising the impairments that linger for some time after an episode of schizophrenia. It is also necessary to point out that if the relative always takes over from the patient, the patient will never improve. These messages need to be reiterated many times before relatives' behaviour begins to change. Persistence is one of the greatest therapeutic virtues in this work.

In order to get the patient to spend more time away from a parent, therapists help to establish links with people of the patient's generation. This is often impeded by the small social networks that patients sustain and by lack of social skills. Sometimes a healthy sibling can be recruited as an ally to take the patient out and to introduce them to healthy young people. However, siblings may be understandably reluctant to bring their friends and the patient together, particularly if the latter is behaving oddly. Therapists can always fall back on introducing the patient to a day centre or drop-in centre, although a more 'healthy' environment is preferable. It is also helpful to find an interest that existed before the illness supervened and to encourage the patient to take it up again. Sometimes patients can be persuaded to join classes that cater for their interest.

Strategic moves

During the course of family sessions we use a number of strategies directed at facilitating separation. These are used sparingly and with careful judgement as to the right moment to bring them into the session.

Changing seats

The therapists observe the seating arrangements in each session, as this is quite revealing of family relationships. Overinvolved relatives commonly sit next to patients, and may make regular physical contact with them. At an appropriate juncture one of the two co-therapists will suggest changing seats with the parent or the patient. It is remarkable what a dramatic difference this physical separation can make to family interaction.

Splitting up the family

The therapists offer to see the patient separately from the relative. This emphasises that each person has different needs, and has aspects of themselves that are appropriately kept private from the other person. If both parents are present in the household, the therapists will see them together to strengthen the marital alliance. If there is a healthy sibling available, the therapists may suggest that he or she is seen together with the patient to facilitate peer bonding.

Recounting past separations

It can be helpful to ask overinvolved relatives to give an account of how they separated from their parents. This reminds the relative that such a separation is possible and desirable, and puts it in perspective as a normal stage in the development of every individual.

Paradoxical injunctions

When everything else has failed and we cannot think of any other means, we use a paradoxical injunction. We use this technique rarely because it works through the family members being unaware of what they are doing or why they are doing it. Furthermore it enhances the therapists' power at the expense of the family's. In order to construct a bridge between the more usual approaches and a paradoxical injunction, the therapists can introduce it by saying, "It looks like our way of helping you hasn't worked. Let's try it your way – only more so." In the case of over-involvement, we tell the relative and patient that they are not spending enough time together and that they must not let each other out of sight. The intention is that if they really follow this instruction they will get heartily sick of each other and begin to want some time apart. This intervention has worked when nothing else was effective.

Summary

Overinvolved relationships are symmetrical and the anxieties and dependence of both partners need to be addressed. Brief trial separations should be negotiated as a way of tackling the anxieties. Relatives must be encouraged to attend to their own needs and to set limits to the patient's demands. The patient's confidence should be built up and they should be helped to establish social links outside the household. Strategic moves include changing seats during a session, seeing parts of the family separately, and getting relatives to recount past separations.

14 Grief

Grief and loss are common emotions families experience with long-term mental illnesses such as schizophrenia. There are two types of loss: loss of the person they used to know and loss of the hopes and aspirations they had for that person. It is in the nature of the illness that negative symptoms, such as lack of motivation, apathy and social withdrawal, often persist long after the acute phases of the illness have subsided. Hence child care, household responsibilities and employment are all too often affected. The patient may not provide any social company for the family. As a result, families may feel they have lost the person they used to know. Unfortunately the illness often starts in adolescence or early adulthood, when the patient is at a critical stage in life and is expected to achieve most. Hence education, work and relationships are often disrupted. As a result families may feel they have lost all hopes and aspirations for the person. Moreover, their grief is compounded by the fact that, unlike grieving for a deceased person, patients are still alive, only they appear as strangers, many of the familiar aspects of the person having vanished.

Part of the therapists' job is to help families to overcome their grief. Enough rapport has to be developed to enable families to discuss their feelings. Some families may deny that there has been any loss or refuse to acknowledge any possibilities of patients relapsing. Instead, their expectations for patients' performance remain high. Sometimes patients share families' unrealistic expectations and keep trying to achieve well beyond their abilities, leading to frequent disappointments, stresses and relapses. This can lead to a loss of confidence and a negative cycle of hopelessness for both patients and relatives. Some emotionally over-involved relatives tend to refuse to talk about what the patient is like at the moment but hark back constantly to past good memories when the patient was a child. With these families, the therapists' job is to lower their expectations by educating them about the effects of the illness. It may take several months to work through the family's denials.

The main task is to get families to acknowledge the reality of the loss without losing sight of the positive sides that still exist. Families can be encouraged to express their profound feelings of loss and devastation, which could be normalised by the therapists' sharing of their experience of families who have gone through similar stages.

Clinical example
Relatives' feelings of grief were discussed in this group and normalised.
Mrs A. I can't feel the same as I did. Too much has been taken out of me. If anything happened to him I'd be terribly upset, but I don't think it would hurt permanently.
Mrs B. [Interrupts] It would have been a relief dear. I felt this when Andrew was so ill I would rather he had died and I mean that. I didn't want the boy ill like that.
T. It's not unusual to feel like that with these illnesses; it can make you very upset to see people change and then to have to cope with all the problems.

Patients should also be encouraged to share their own experiences of the illness to help their families to understand and empathise. At times it is advisable to do grief work about loss of the person in the relatives' group or separately, as it might be too painful for patients to hear. A relatives' group can be useful to share feelings and to demonstrate how some families might have seen some progress over time, despite their losses. Therapists should convey realistic hope and elicit the advantages of still having the person there. Once families can acknowledge their losses and see the positive attributes left, a structured behavioural strategy using graded tasks could be employed to enable progress, as described in Chapter 8.

Summary

Grief is a common experience in the family when a member suffers from an illness which can be chronic and often disabling. In the case of schizophrenia, it could be grief for the loss of the person they used to know or grief for the loss of the hopes and aspirations for the person. It often is a combination of both. Relatives' groups are safe venues for relatives to express their grief openly without the fear of upsetting patients and to share their feelings. Therapists should encourage families to overcome their grief; to see the positive qualities that the patients still have; and to lower their expectations. Once families can acknowledge their losses and see the positive attributes that remain, small realistic goals can be set to enable progress.

15 The vulnerability of adult patients

When people have been unwell with schizophrenia for some years, they may have residual disabilities which have to be coped with. These can include positive symptoms, such as distressing voices or delusions, poor concentration, and also negative symptoms, such as apathy, low motivation, and self-neglect. Those who had an early onset of illness may always have been socially isolated.

Clinical example
A mother described her schizophrenic daughter's clinging behaviour from an early age.
M. Elaine didn't like her father very much. It's always been me ever since she was born. She was a difficult baby. She screamed and didn't sleep very much as a child, and wherever I went, Elaine had to go. Even when she was young, if I went into friends I was being called out again. You know, the others all played, but not Elaine, "Mum, come in!" It's always been the same with Elaine. Very, very pathetic.

Even with a later onset, we know that social networks become restricted in schizophrenia because it is hard to make new friends, because social withdrawal is quite common, and because of the stigma of mental illness.

For all of these reasons it may be true that patients are not as competent as before the illness; they may have lost skills and confidence, and lack experiences such as being able to live independently. Carers who live with such patients, particularly carers who are parents, may find it difficult to assess accurately the level of residual problems, and to encourage and allow social functioning to recover. This is often part of overinvolvement, in that the parent may not accept adult functioning in the patient and may continue to treat them as a child. This is discussed in Chapter 13.

However, it can also happen that carers perceive accurately that patients are not able to cope with various problems. Therapists need to achieve a balance between encouraging as much independence as possible, while acknowledging with the patient and relatives that there are problems that will continue to need help from carers. At best patients can be encouraged to specify and ask for this help, and over time the level can be reduced. In other cases patients are not allowed to even try things for themselves, and in this pattern patients themselves may see no need to change anything; they may be perfectly comfortable with the status quo.

Sexuality

An area where the issue of actual dependence versus fears of vulnerability is highlighted is that of sexuality. Parents, particularly of adult daughters, may find it extremely difficult to cope with the fact that the patient is likely to have sexual needs, and further, many choose as partners people who would not previously have been welcomed to the family unit. In long-established illness, partners are likely to be other patients, who may have as many as or even more problems than the patient. Another pattern is for sexual contacts to be casual rather than permanent, as intense relationships may be difficult to manage. Unprotected sexual contacts carry the risk of disease, such as AIDS, and also of pregnancy. Both of these raise understandable fears in carers.

Therapists should aim to allow for a realistic and frank discussion of sexual needs in adult patients. It is not an issue for all patients, as for some, social withdrawal and their own reticence will preclude it. However, for others it may be the first chance they have had to discuss it at all with their relatives. Sexuality needs privacy, and acceptance by the rest of the family. Ways of achieving this may have to be discussed. The fears families may have about the risk of disease and pregnancy should be brought into the open. Often patients have taken responsibility for themselves, but have not mentioned it, or are not believed; this should be clarified. Usually families' worst fears are not realistic and the likelihood of various negative outcomes should be looked at.

Pregnancy raises particular worries, including the possibility of whether the baby will inherit the illness; whether the patient will be able to look after a baby, or whether the carers will have to take on yet another job; whether the patient should have the baby at all. Again, these need to be brought out and the family encouraged to discuss the options and come to some agreement. Usually the patient is the best person to do this, and by encouraging this, therapists reinforce the responsible and adult side of a patient's behaviour.

Some families may refuse to talk about sexuality. It may be felt to be too painful, it may be culturally unacceptable, or it may be seen as inappropriate. Any problems will be denied. It is not necessary to insist that a family face these issues, but if it is an area where the family identify problems, then therapists should help to facilitate solutions.

Social competence

Another area of vulnerability may be social competence. Can a patient manage the usual problems that many adults have to deal with – managing money, coping with more competent friends, not being exploited by others?

Clinical example
This illustrates a mother's anxieties about her son's ability to budget.
T. So what are the things that James already has going for him? He can prepare his own meals?
M. Oh yes. He prepares them alright. Gets his clothes in the washing machine. He can iron. Well, he's ironing because he was at cubs. You should see these uniforms: he does them beautiful. That part's alright, but the money part. To save. If he got fifty pounds, he'd go out there tonight and spend the fifty pounds. And I think it's because he knows he can come and live here. Whereas if someone was going to say, "Where's my rent?" or "I take it away from you," they'd be more responsible.
T. So you have some fears about his not being able to budget.

There may be particular (and possibly valid) fears that a patient will be mugged when going down the street, that they cannot manage things like bus rides, or trips out; sometimes even crossing the road is felt to be too risky. Again, as in overinvolvement, the reality and likelihood of a negative outcome should be discussed, and fears of a 'disaster' looked at calmly. The patient's views, while not always realistic themselves, should be taken seriously and therapists should try to use them as the agent of change whenever possible. As usual, fears should be narrowed down from the general ('He might get run over') to the specific ('How can we help him to get used to crossing roads?') and then the real problems, if they exist, can gradually be worked on.

The aim of the therapist with these issues is to encourage realistic but achievable aims which help a patient begin to function as an adult again, despite any residual problems. While this may not be possible to achieve in all areas of functioning (long-term patients may always need help with some aspects of daily living), often there are islands of competence and these need to be noted and developed.

Summary

Many families have to help patients to cope with residual disabilities. It can be difficult for relatives to assess these accurately and to help patients recover as much independence and adult functioning as possible. Two particularly difficult areas are the sexual needs of patients and their social competence. Therapists need to encourage families to focus on these problems and aim at achievable solutions.

16 Stigma

Society by and large still has a stereotyped view of the mentally ill. In the case of schizophrenia, the beliefs that these patients are violent, show sexually inappropriate behaviour, or suffer from split personality still prevail. This is further complicated by the unpredictability of the illness. Some sufferers may relapse quite suddenly, and the cause of the relapse may not always be clear. Some chronic sufferers may be stigmatised because they display the obvious residual negative symptoms of self-neglect, lack of motivation, social withdrawal, and odd or bizarre behaviour. Rigidity or tremor as a result of side-effects of major tranquillisers may also lead to stigmatisation. Sometimes the sufferer's sense of being stigmatised may be based on past disturbed behaviour which was socially unacceptable.

Furthermore, there is still often an assumption that families may have caused schizophrenia in some ways. Some families, particularly Asian families, may believe that if the offspring suffers from a major mental illness, the whole family has failed or 'lost face'. It is still common in Western culture for parents to believe that they must have failed to some extent in bringing up the child for him or her to suffer from schizophrenia.

As a result, families and patients may feel rejection, real or perceived, by relatives, friends, and society as a whole. The sense of rejection is often mixed with feelings of guilt, anger, inadequacy, or hopelessness. Sometimes families only tell close relatives or friends about the illness. If patients have been admitted to a psychiatric hospital or psychiatric ward, some families ensure that nobody outside the family knows about it. Because of the sense of failure and fear of not being accepted by others, families often isolate themselves. They avoid contact with people who they fear might look down on them. Some families even go to the extreme of moving to a new neighbourhood in order to conceal the fact that their relative has had a major nervous breakdown.

Intervention

It is important to explore the sense of stigmatisation and isolation with families. Sometimes families may not say that they feel stigmatised but behave as if they were by isolating themselves from larger networks, from which they could receive support and social company to enrich the quality of their lives. Education helps to demystify the illness and get rid of the guilty feeling that it is the families who cause the illness. It also helps to normalise families' feelings. However, the two initial education sessions are often not enough, and therapists may have to relate information explicitly to the specific family problem of how the illness is construed. Relatives' groups are often a good arena for relatives to share and normalise their feelings, grievances and past experiences.

Clinical example
This example is taken from an interchange in a relatives' group.

Mrs M. I can't have Elaine with other relatives because they get very irritable. They don't understand Elaine and even shoot questions at her. They think that pushing her is helping her, which it isn't.

Mrs T. I'm very sensitive to the fact that our visitors would perhaps put Robin on edge and set him back. I find that I'm embarrassed a little bit because my relatives have to sort of make allowances for Robin.

Mrs M. We all want our children to be better and to behave normal and be like us. But all the time we're aware that they're ill and we're making up excuses, really, either for ourselves or for others, for people not to notice that our children are ill.

Mrs T. You can't treat people like that! They would know, and you embarrass them by trying to do it.

Relatives in a later group discuss the stigma of mental illness, and the need to explain to the neighbours.

Mrs A. I don't hide the facts.

Mrs B. I carry on as normally as possible.

T.   What do you tell people?

Mr B. That Peter is sick and had a breakdown, had schizophrenia.

Mrs B. But people don't know what you're talking about with schizophrenia.

Mr B. Nervous breakdown seems to be accepted. But the trouble is there is nothing wrong with him, he's a fine-looking chap.

Mrs A. I think you have to let other people know what's wrong with them. You have to explain if they don't know about it. I told a friend at work and they were quite sympathetic.

More sensitive issues, such as incest, or problems that are uncommon to the rest of the group, such as an offspring or a sibling being the sole carer, may not be discussed. Therapists need to be alert and sensitive to these issues and deal with them within the individual family setting.

To help patients break out of isolation, therapists need to be sensitive as well as persevering. Patients may have had years of isolation, as a result of which they are likely to lack confidence in their social competence. Patients may be easily embarrassed or intimidated. They may fear that they will be rejected because they have had the experience of a mental breakdown. Their fear may also come from past experiences of psychotic symptoms causing social embarrassment. Thus therapists should be empathic but encourage realistic expectations. Going through the advantages and disadvantages of continuing to isolate oneself from a larger network might help. Patients should be persuaded that the occasional symptom does not necessarily impede their ability to socialise. However, with some patients, there might be a genuine lack of social skills rather than a lack of motivation. In these cases therapists should resort to social skills training. Graded tasks and task assignments as experiments can help to persuade patients to go out and mix more easily. Initially therapists or family members may have to accompany patients on the first couple of outings. Furthermore, therapists need to persuade patients to talk to the appropriate people in the right context about their experience of mental illness without feeling shame. The idea is that patients would have the choice of telling people about their experience or not, without feeling that the experience is so shaming that they have to conceal it under all circumstances. To do so would negate any opportunities for support from any informal network.

Helping carers to form relationships outside the immediate family is an important aspect of family work if isolation is a problem. At times it is difficult to tease out whether isolation results from a sense of stigmatisation or from overinvolvement. However, families often cope better if there is a larger network from which they can ask for help or find relief. The usual excuses for not going out are "I'm too tired," "I haven't got enough time," "My son needs me," or "He can't be left on his own". There may be an element of truth in this, but it is important for therapists to push so that families can break out of their isolation. It often helps to improve the quality of their relationships, reduce the burden on relatives, reduce overinvolvement and reinforce generational boundaries. Sometimes it is useful to frame it as "Everyone in the family needs to look after themselves in order to cope". Hence neither patients nor relatives are singled out. In some very entrenched families, therapists may have to frame it in altruistic terms, such as "You need to look after yourself to help the patient," or "The patient needs to be on her own to promote independent functioning".

Just as with patients, relatives need to be persuaded to test their beliefs that people would reject or look down on them because they have a schizophrenic relative. Cognitive–behavioural techniques of gentle persuasion to undertake short outings to test out their fears and then gradually to increase the difficulty of tasks applies equally to relatives and patients.

Summary

Many families feel stigmatised and isolated. As a result, they often avoid contact with people from whom they could receive support and social company. Helping carers and patients to break out of their isolation is an important aspect of family work. Sometimes it is difficult to tease out whether carers do not go out because of emotional overinvolvement or fear of rejection. Therapists need to inquire explicitly and deal with the cause accordingly. Some patients lack social skills or confidence because of the chronicity of their illness. A cognitive–behavioural technique of setting graded realistic tasks is useful to test out their beliefs of being looked down upon and to encourage both carers and patients to venture out.

17 Absent family members

How to get everyone in the family involved

As discussed in Chapter 2, recruitment of families should be attempted at a time of crisis, when families feel the need of professional help most. Most families first come into contact with services after a period of disturbance at home, during which virtually everyone in the family will have been affected by the patient's disturbed behaviour. The practice of beginning family work with education also helps to get every family member involved. Therapists should send families the message that it is important for all members to be present so that everyone has some understanding of what the illness is. During the education sessions, there should be a strong message that every family member can help by creating a supportive and encouraging environment to prevent relapse. It should be emphasised that:

(a) the family is not sick and hence is not being treated
(b) therapists are there to deal with some of the problems they have as a result of a family member suffering from schizophrenia
(c) relatives are valuable assets and allies of the professionals in helping patients.

In this way the logic of getting everyone actively involved is made clear to them. The emphasis on a positive approach and collaboration during therapy also helps to engage family members. Therapists should be sensitive to families' needs and emphasise strengths of the family. Time should be spent listening to the family's experience and the involvement of each individual member so that the family feel they are listened to and understood. Similarly, family members' past attempts should be listened to and respected as their best effort to cope, no matter how undesirable these might seem to therapists. In order to establish alliances with individual members, therapists should understand the ongoing family issues as well as the demands on and problems of each family member. Hence it is quite a demanding task to establish rapport with each family member, as well as with the family as an entity. Moreover therapy goals and tasks should be set only after each family member's view has been sought and disagreements resolved.

Involving the 'peripheral' family network for support

The definition of 'family' varies in different cultures. Relatives who are counted as peripheral family members by most people in Britain may be seen by others as close family members who are actively involved in family matters. If there is a family crisis, distant relatives may rally round quickly to help out. Hence they are often useful resources for the family. This is particularly true for families who have immigrated to Britain. Peripheral family may be a useful support.

Clinical example
T.   Do you have any relatives that you can ask for help?
Mrs A. Well yes I suppose I do have my cousin in Croydon. I can go and see her for a break, or get on the phone.

Even within Britain, white British people in different parts of the country may include different people when they use the term 'family'. Hence therapists should be sensitive to this issue and inquire who is around and involved in helping patients. Sometimes the important people are identified in the course of discussing families' past attempts to cope. Important people in the network should be invited to family meetings even though they are not close relatives.

Coping with non-attendance

Non-attendance of family members cannot be ignored and should be dealt with as it occurs to give the clear message that everyone is important and their active involvement is needed to help patients. Relatives may be out of the house during the time of the meeting, or sometimes hover around in the next room making their presence known and yet do not come into the meeting. In either case they should be invited to join the meetings.

Relatives may not attend family sessions for a variety of reasons. It could be that the person concerned has missed a meeting and the date of the following meeting is not passed on. This might reflect an overinvolved relative's attitude that they can deal with the patient's problem best on their own. They may feel that there is no need to involve other family members, hence dates of future meetings are not conveyed to them. The simplest way to deal with this is to say that therapists understand there is a lot going on for the family and perhaps it is difficult for them at the moment to organise everyone to be there. Therapists might offer to write to each member individually for a limited time to establish regular attendance. It could also be a reflection on the therapeutic relationship if the individuals concerned feel they have been poorly understood or attacked unfairly in previous meetings. Or it could be that the absent members do not appreciate their role in helping the patient or that they simply do not understand or value the help being offered. Regular feedback from relatives, both verbal and written, help to alert therapists to these problems.

If it is a relationship issue, the person's feeling should be accepted and validated. Therapists should make clear the intentions of what they did in previous sessions, and could even acknowledge that their actions unfortunately might not have the desired effect. Most people will respond positively to this type of genuine and open approach. If the reason for non-attendance is not seeing the value of family meetings or their involvement, the rationale should be reiterated and any personal concerns or worries worked through. Sometimes, relatives do not attend meetings because of their fear of change. The fear could be based on the experience that patients relapsed in the past during times of change. Therapists should reassure them that gradual change is often productive and does not necessarily lead to relapse, particularly if there is a supportive environment.

Another type of fear is that overinvolved relatives are often not sure what their life would be like if the patient became more independent. This can be dealt with as described in Chapter 13. Lastly, relatives sometimes continue to be absent despite a lot of effort to get them to attend. Realistically therapists have no option but to persevere with parts of the family. Often the non-attendants eventually come through curiosity or because they find they are affected by these meetings as a result of changes in other members. If members refuse to attend despite being asked repeatedly, this may have to be accepted eventually. Whatever the reasons may be for non-attendance, when the members concerned start to attend meetings, therapists should be warm and welcoming. Their efforts in attending meetings should be appreciated. Therapists should not necessarily accept any excuses for non-attendance at face value. Often, non-attendance is connected with other important family issues which those concerned do not want to reveal and these possibilities should be considered.

Coping with lack of interest in meetings

Sometimes relatives come to meetings and yet show distinct lack of interest. They can be silent all through meetings and be reluctant to express their opinions even when asked. At the extreme, some relatives doze off or read the newspaper during family meetings. At other times family members, particularly the patient, might want to leave in the middle of the meeting. If this happens, an attempt should always be made to ask them to return, preferably by another family member. If this is not possible, one of the therapists should approach them to ask them to return. This emphasises that their presence is important in the meeting even if they refuse to come back. Non-verbal messages like leaving the meeting or reading the newspaper should be explored and clarified. The message could be that they felt misunderstood, undervalued, or they simply do not understand the help being offered and what is expected of them. These could be dealt with as outlined above. Should therapists allow such lack of interest to persist, relatives may exaggerate their behaviour in order to get their message through, do something else to sabotage therapists' efforts to help, or simply stop attending family meetings altogether.

Summary

Engagement is often helped by the message that therapists are not there to treat the family but to deal with some of the problems they have as a result of a member suffering from schizophrenia. Relatives should be seen as assets and allies of the professional to help patients. The definition of 'family' can be quite loose; important but distant relatives should be identified and be included in meetings. Non-attendance of family members should be treated seriously and therapists should try their best to make sure that every family member attends regularly. Similarly, lack of interest during family meetings should be explored and the message dealt with accordingly.

18 Helping marital families

Although many of the problems that arise in marital households are the same as in parental households, there are also some important differences that need to be considered. Spouses can be just as critical as parents, but are much less likely to be overinvolved. On the rare occasions when overinvolvement is found in spouses, they have often adopted a parenting role in respect to the patient.

Task sharing

As with parents, criticism from a spouse is usually directed at the patient's negative symptoms. If the patient is inactive, this has an effect on the household economy, and shifts the whole burden of wage earning and house keeping onto the spouse. In addition, there may of course be the responsibilities of child care. Sometimes other relatives, such as the spouse's or patient's parents, may be available to help. It can happen that the patient is left without a contributory role in the family, which in itself is demoralising. In approaching this problem it is important to encourage the family members to be as flexible as possible. Reversal of conventional roles may be a solution, the wife going out to work while the husband cares for the home or children, or both. If this is not possible for a male patient, it is helpful to negotiate carrying out tasks which represent a valued contribution, such as decorating a room, mending or fixing things.

Clinical example
In this session, therapists are helping a husband and wife negotiate a task.
T. So Amos, you've said that it would be helpful if you'd be more able to do the task that Amy asked you to do, if she assists you with it.

68

P. Yeah, sometimes.
T. Amy how do you feel about that, about helping him?
W. I don't mind, no.
T. How would you feel about it though if Amos was to mow the lawn for you despite the fact you have different ways of doing it.
W. Oh it don't matter how you cut the grass really does it? It would just be nice if he did it.

For a female patient undertaking a conventional role, help may be required with improving skills in shopping, budgeting, and cooking. It is important for the therapists to distinguish between the lack of opportunity to exercise a skill, as can happen with an overprotective relative, and a basic lack of the necessary skill. In the former case, work with the family is indicated. In the latter case, the therapists should consider referral of the patient to an occupational therapy department or day centre. As always, the healthy spouse should be encouraged to reward the patient with praise for successfully completing small tasks.

In the unusual situation that the spouse is overinvolved, they will need to be persuaded to give up some of the responsibility they have shouldered for the patient. The approach is the same as with overinvolved parents, namely to explore the relative's anxieties about the possible dangers of giving the patient more scope, to give the relative permission to off-load some of the responsibility, and to encourage the partners to try out a small shift in the balance of responsibility. Pressure from other relatives in the relatives' group can be a potent force for producing change in this area.

Loss of a confidante

A warm and mutually supportive relationship is the basis for a good marriage. Schizophrenia can erode this basis by impairing the patient's emotional responsiveness to their spouse and their ability to provide support. The spouse may find it difficult to accept that the loss of what they valued in the marriage is a result of the illness and not a deliberate withholding by the patient. It is not uncommon to find a high-EE spouse harbouring a deep sense of disappointment and even bitterness.

Research has shown that depression is associated with the lack of a confiding relationship. If schizophrenia makes it impossible for the patient to fulfil this role, the spouse should be encouraged to find someone of the same sex as themselves who can act as a confidante. A confidante of the opposite sex might make the patient jealous and genuinely threaten their relationship with the spouse. Spouses may find an appropriate confidante through the relatives' group.

Re-establishing a warm relationship

We have generally found that if relatives' critical attitudes can be moderated, warmth towards the patient returns spontaneously. In the case of parents this is a consequence of the natural investment of positive emotions in their child. In marital partners, however, the warmth would have had to be present in the relationship at the beginning to re-emerge. If the marital relationship was not particularly warm to start with, the best one can hope to achieve is the sharing of tasks in a neutral atmosphere. If the relationship was initially warm, it might still require a special effort to resuscitate it. Three main strategies can be employed.

(a) Ask each partner to say something positive about the other person. If they complain that they cannot think of anything positive in the current relationship, then ask them to remember a positive aspect of the person in the past.

(b) Ask each partner to say something they would like the other person to do for them and negotiate for this to be carried out. Make sure that the task is well within the person's capabilities. Even a simple activity such as making a cup of tea for the other person can shift the relationship in a more positive direction.

(c) Find something that the partners would enjoy doing together outside the home, and set them the task of trying it. As before, if they assert that there is nothing at present that they enjoy together, get them to review the history of their relationship to find a suitable activity.

Sexuality

Both the patient and spouse may be reluctant to raise the issue of their sexual relationship, but it is important for the therapists to introduce it tactfully. Schizophrenia itself can diminish libido, but so can neuroleptic drugs, and in men they can inhibit erection and ejaculation. If any of these problems exist, the possible causes should be presented to the partners and the patient's medication should be reviewed. A spouse may interpret a diminution in their partner's sexual interest and activity as a sign of loss of love and affection. It is therefore important that the alternative explanations should be given to them.

If alterations in the drug regime are not helpful or not possible, and the partners want further help with their sexual relationship, referral to a therapist specialising in sexual problems is indicated.

Clinical example

Relationships can often suffer after a long illness. This was discussed in some detail in one group meeting, where a wife found her husband's renewed sexual interest in her very difficult to cope with.

T. There's a point here about giving support. You don't want to give support Mrs A and you two [Mr and Mrs B] find you are arguing about the amount of support John [son] needs.

Mrs A. But there's a lot of feeling between you two [Mr and Mrs B]. Hugh idolises me and I don't hate the sight of him, but as far as being a husband and wife goes there's a lot been killed off, and I feel at times as if I've been cut into little pieces and they've all got a piece each and I'm just not me. . . .

T. Did you [Mrs D] find it a problem when your husband was out of hospital?

Mrs D. Yes it was at first.

T. Did you find that the relationship built up again?

Mrs D. No not quite. It got better but it took a long time.

Mrs A. He came to meet me the other night. It sounds nice but I can't even walk home on my own any more.

T. It sounds as if you've got used to managing things by yourself.

Mrs A. I have. After all this time, its a weird feeling that Hugh can even feel this way.

Mrs D. It sounds like a good sign.

Mrs A. It's a good sign for him getting better but its a terrifying sign for me if I can't put back what he wants, and I don't really think I can. I would be his best friend, but if he wants more than that I don't really think I can cope with it.

T. Have you said to him that you might build up the relationship gradually? Do you think it might be easier if you took it in stages?

Separation

In a parental household, one of the major aims is to increase the independence of patients, with the possible result that they set up a household of their own. We would not start out with the aim of separating spouses, although this outcome is usually raised by one or both partners during the course of work with them. Sometimes, despite the best efforts of the therapists, the partners remain irreconcilable. Under these circumstances it is desirable for the therapists to help them to separate in as constructive a manner as possible. This will usually involve assisting the spouse to express guilt about deserting the patient, and exploring anxieties about the possible disastrous outcomes, such as suicide or vagrancy. Spouses rarely have the same degree of commitment to patients as parents do, so that if they separate, the spouse is unlikely to provide much ongoing support for the patient. Possible sources of emotional and practical support for patients need to be identified and brought into the picture, so that they are not left completely isolated.

If there are children in the household, their welfare also must be considered (Chapter 19).

Summary

There are some specific problems that arise in marital households. These include sharing the burdens of wage earning and house keeping, the spouse's loss of a confidante, and the effects of the illness and its drug treatment on the couple's sexual relationship. Therapists need to work towards re-establishing a warm relationship between the partners. Occasionally their task is to help the couple separate as painlessly as possible. If there are partners in a group it can be a safe place in which to discuss marital difficulties.

19   Children in the household

The children of a schizophrenic parent may be adults, in which case they often take on some of the roles of carers. This is discussed in Chapter 20. However, if they are under the age of 16, there are a number of issues concerning their emotional development which need to be considered by the therapists. If there are young children in the household, social services are quite likely to be involved, or if not, may need to become involved. Hence the therapists should be prepared to develop a close liaison with social services.

Some 40 years ago it was relatively rare to find young children in a household with a schizophrenic parent. With the increasing implementation of community care, this situation is becoming more common.

Timing of parents' marriage

The most usual circumstance is that the parents married when they were both well and that one of them subsequently developed schizophrenia. Children of the marriage are likely to have experienced normal parenting for a period before the onset of the illness. Their response to the illness will depend, of course, on their age at the time, but also on the way in which the other parent responds to it. The onset of schizophrenia often creates anxiety and confusion in the marital partner, who may, as a result, be unable to help the children deal with their own emotions. Therefore it may be necessary for the therapists to spend time with the children, encouraging them to express their understanding of their parent's illness and their responses to it.

If the parents married when one was already ill, the well parent may have known what they were taking on and would be able to explain it to the children when they reached an appropriate age. On the other hand, the children will never have experienced continuous normal parenting from one of their parents and may have suffered a variety of deprivations as a result. There will also have been considerable strain on the well parent from caring for their sick partner and trying to fill both paternal and maternal roles. If they have not already recruited friends or relatives to help with the care of the children, the therapists should stimulate them to do so.

It is becoming increasingly common that people with schizophrenia and other severe psychiatric illnesses meet in psychiatric facilities and form partnerships. In some of these families, children are born and we have already worked with several such families.

Clinical example

A daughter describes how she and her sister manage; both parents met in hospital.

Daughter. Mum's had problems. So has Dad sometimes. We just have to manage. Some days are fine, and my sister visits when she can. I did leave home 18 months ago. But it didn't work out. Mum came round and phoned up all the time so I moved back in.

The children have massive obstacles to overcome in order to achieve a normal development, not the least of which is the dawning realisation that their parents are not like other children's parents. Such children will have been designated as at risk from the beginning of their lives, with a consequent involvement of social services. However, there is still likely to be work for the therapists to undertake on the current understanding the children have of their parents' illnesses. Even where only a single parent, usually a mother, is ill, again social services will be intimately involved with the family and a considered decision will have been taken shortly after each child's birth to keep mother and child together.

Sometimes a child will have been removed from a schizophrenic mother and placed with another relative by social services. This may be a grandparent or sibling of the patient. A tense relationship can develop between the patient and relative over the care of the child, corresponding to other 'tug-of-love' situations. This is often made worse by the relative citing the patient's illness as a reason to criticise her mothering ability. Of course there may be a basis for this, but if the relative is found to be critical of or hostile to the patient they will need to be worked with like any other high-EE relative.

Exposure of the child to symptoms

Some patients are able to keep their delusions and hallucinations to themselves except when acutely ill. Others find it hard to contain the experiences and are prone to talk to any family member about them, or even to people outside the family. Children exposed to a parent's delusions or hallucinations are likely to be very upset and frightened by them. They may not have been able to formulate them as symptoms of an illness. Therapists should allow children to express their feelings concerning the symptoms their parent has told them about, and should be given an understandable illness model to fit them into. It is not uncommon for a child to develop a feeling of responsibility for causing the parent's illness, attributing it to their own bad behaviour. This needs to be thoroughly explored and appropriate reassurance and explanation provided.

As with adult relatives, children may find it difficult to view negative symptoms as part of an illness. Furthermore they may be affected by having an inactive, emotionally unresponsive parent as a role model. The positive aspects of the ill parent should be emphasised and the children helped to relate to them. They may need another role model of the same sex to assist them with their own development.

Factors influencing the child's response to a schizophrenic parent

The course of the parent's illness clearly has an important effect. With intermittent illnesses, the child can experience the parent as being relatively well between episodes, and can learn to identify the behaviour that is part of the illness. However, if the illness is continuous, the child has the much more difficult task of distinguishing those aspects of the parent which are healthy from those which are sick. This is something that the therapists can provide assistance with.

The patient's degree of insight is also important, as it will determine the extent to which the pathological experiences are shared with the children.

The spouse's attitude will influence the children's approach to the sick parent. If the spouse is critical or hostile, the children may adopt the same attitude or may attempt to defend the sick parent. An overinvolved spouse may collude with their partner's delusions or hallucinations, increasing the children's difficulty in establishing reality testing.

Another dimension is added to the problem if the children are incorporated in the parent's delusional system, for example by becoming the object of paranoid or sexual delusions. Under these circumstances, separation of the children from the sick parent should be seriously considered.

Specific problems

Parental conflict

This is relatively common in high-EE families, and there is always the risk that it will lead to violence. Children in the household are likely to be frightened by the threat or actuality of violence between their parents. Therapists will always take a firm line against the escalation of conflict, but this is even more important when there are young children present.

Parental absence

The inevitable absences of a sick parent due to hospital admissions are certain to have an effect on children. The healthy parent should be encouraged to take the children to visit the other in hospital, with suitable preparation about the nature of the ward. Sometimes children develop a fear that the sick parent will be taken away for ever. Visits to the parent in hospital can be reassuring.

Unfortunately suicide is common in schizophrenia, the lifetime rate being about 10%. If this tragedy occurs the surviving parent may not be in a state of mind to deal with the child's grief and need to mourn. The therapists may need to attend to this or refer the child to an appropriate specialist.

Parental preoccupation

The needs of the sick adult may take up a lot of the healthy partner's emotional energy, thus interfering with their parenting ability. This may lead to emotional deprivation of the children. Furthermore, one of the children, usually the oldest, may take on a parenting role in relation to the other siblings. There may also be pressure on one or more of the children to act in a parental role towards the sick parent. Premature parenting is likely to interfere with the normal emotional development of a child. The therapists may be able to deal with this problem by changing the balance of care in the family, but sometimes a child may need referral to the appropriate psychiatric facility.

A related problem is the need a child may experience to protect their parent's reputation and authority against the teasing of other children at school. It will be helpful in this instance for the therapists to discuss with the family the origins of stigma and the reasons why people need to make fun of the mentally ill. It can be useful to request the child's head teacher or teacher to initiate discussion in the school on this topic. The therapists should be prepared to offer some input into such a discussion.

Concern about inheritance or contagion

Older children may express a fear of catching mental illness, or may be worried about inheritance. A frank discussion of the risks to children of a schizophrenic parent (about 8%) should be offered by the therapists, couched in terms that the children will understand. Some children may worry about passing the illness on to their own offspring. They can be reassured that the risk is no more than 2%, that is, twice the risk in the general population.

Summary

Children who have a schizophrenic parent are likely to face a variety of problems to do with impaired parenting. This may result from the direct effect of the illness on the affected parent or the indirect effect on the healthy parent. Children will have to cope with absences when the parent is in hospital, and possibly with exposure to the symptoms of schizophrenia. The therapists need to provide them with an age-appropriate explanation of the illness. Family work can help children resolve their problems but they might require referral to a child guidance clinic.

20 Carers who are siblings or children

Occasionally the main carer in a household is a sibling of the patient or an adult child. There are specific problems peculiar to these relationships which are not shared by parents or spouses.

Siblings

Siblings are not as committed to the patient as are parents, who have cared for the patient since childhood, or spouses, who have chosen their partner. We have never encountered an overinvolved sibling, but siblings can be highly critical. In the normal course of their development siblings would be expected to develop heterosexual relationships of their own outside the household. They may feel inhibited from doing this by the demands that the patient's care makes on them, or by their reluctance to acquire something that is out of the patient's reach. This can lead to resentment of the patient and a critical attitude.

Clinical example
A brother talks about having to look after his youngest sister.
Mr A. We've always been together. I've always had to look after her. It's just been a duty, something that I've had to take on once our mother died. It's not as if I had a choice. I've just had to put up with how difficult she can be.

The therapists' aims are to reduce the responsibility the sibling takes for the patient and encourage them to attend to their own needs. In parallel with this, the therapists need to build up the patient's confidence in looking after themselves.

Sometimes siblings find themselves thrust into the role of carer through death of parents. They may feel guilty about their previous intention to be as uninvolved with the patient as possible and swing to the other extreme in trying to replace the parents. If they are married, their spouse is likely to be resentful of the new focus of attention. The therapists' task is to make siblings feel that their efforts are valued, but to moderate the amount they try to do for the patient, and to develop the patient's sense of autonomy. It may be difficult to persuade siblings to give up some of their responsibility for the patient if they have chosen this as their role in life, and partic-ularly if they have some moral backing for it, for instance, 'duty as a Christian'.

Children

When a parent suffers from schizophrenia, adult children are likely to show different attitudes and adopt varying roles. One at least will probably accept a caring role, though it depends a great deal on how able the other parent is to fulfil this function. If the other parent is physically or mentally ill, or absent for some reason, the whole burden is likely to fall on one of the children. The response can be to take over a parental role completely, and to show overinvolved behaviour and attitudes. This is likely to entail poorly expressed feelings, particularly resentment at having to relinquish the role of a child in the family prematurely. The carer may also experience the loss of a parent to give advice and guidance, and may lack an adequate role model for parenting. Therapists should be prepared to help the carer with grieving for the 'lost' parent and resentment about the untimely role reversal.

The carer is likely to experience anxieties about ever being able to live their own life or to leave to set up a family of their own. The therapists need to address the usual issues of giving the carer permission to relinquish some responsibility for the sick parent, and helping to relieve guilt. If there are other siblings around, the therapists should try to recruit them to share some of the responsibility, and thus give the caring child respite. If no other sibling is available, professional agencies should be brought in to give the carer some relief. As always, work should be directed towards helping patients to become more able to look after themselves.

Summary

Siblings who are carers may have dedicated their life to look after the patient, while adult children are likely to experience anxieties about being imprisoned in the caring role. In both instances, the therapeutic aim is to increase the patient's capacity for independence and to relieve the carer of some of the burden of responsibility.

21 Employment

Helping patients to gain outside employment or return to education

The effect of schizophrenia can be very crippling, particularly for those patients with negative symptoms. Some patients may never have had the experience of employment for any length of time if the illness started during adolescence. In any case, starting a new job or returning to full-time education after a long absence can be stressful for anyone. It is a big step, with a significant risk of relapse if not handled carefully. In a relatives' group suggestions can be made from other relatives' experiences of trying to interest a patient in some occupation.

Clinical example
T. What sort of jobs is Richard going for?
Mrs A. Does he fancy library work? It's easy sitting at a desk.
Mrs B. Is he interested in any adult education?
Mrs C. He has ideas one minute and the next morning he doesn't want to.
Mr B. I go to a woodwork thing. It's very easy going. They don't do anything like that?
Mrs C. He keeps on joining evening classes.
Mr B. No, I meant during the day.
T. When did he last try? Why don't you suggest it to him?

The skills necessary to be in employment or education are complex. They include good time keeping, tolerance of some sort of routine, a large degree of independence while away from home, reasonable motivation to do well, ability to pay attention to details, ability to understand and incorporate advice or feedback from supervisors or teachers, and ability to communicate and mix with fellow workers or pupils. Hence it should be attempted only if patients have been stable for several months and everyone in the family agrees to it, so that other family members can provide support and take part in problem solving. Furthermore, patients should be able to recognise early signs of the illness and be able to deal with them. Some families may be impatient and want patients to go back to work or school and get on with life. Others might be hesitant, perhaps because of past experience that patients may not be able to bear the stress, and relapse, requiring the family to deal with the illness all over again. In either case, the family should be persuaded to adopt the graded behavioural approach discussed in Chapter 8.

Preparation of patients

Because of the complexity of skills required for employment or education, preparation should be over a period of time. Again, it is a good idea to frame starting work or education as a trial so that failures can be put into context. A behavioural approach of small steps with increasing difficulty tailored to the individual is useful. To begin with, chores at home can be used as practice for concentration, independence, taking responsibility, and tolerance of routine. As time goes by, the number of tasks and the length of time needed can be increased gradually. Homework practice can also involve patients getting up at a certain time to accomplish certain tasks. Attendance at day centres for industrial or educational programmes is good practice for time keeping, tolerance of routine, and sticking to jobs outside the home before patients finally face the world outside. Therapists should be prepared to provide support and be available during this difficult period.

An immediate issue when applying for jobs is whether to tell potential employers about past psychiatric history. There is no clear-cut answer to that problem. The advantage of telling the truth is that employers may be more supportive or sympathetic, particularly during a time of stress. However, the danger is that it will jeopardise patients' chance of employment. Some employers may not consider employing someone with a significant past psychiatric illness at all. Hence some patients prefer to gloss over the issue. Whatever happens, it has to be a decision made by patients themselves. A discussion about the pros and cons with family members present will enable patients to make an informed decision.

As usual, families should be warned of the difficulties and complexity involved so that they can be prepared for setbacks. To begin with, a part-time job or returning to education part time may be less risky. For some patients, because of negative symptoms or deterioration in skills, realistically they may have to look for a less ambitious job than they had previously. This may create problems for both patients and other family members, particularly if patients come from a professional background. It may take a lot of discussion and exploration of feelings for them to come to terms with the fact that patients may not be as capable or skilled as they used to be. However, most families are able to accept it in the end, particularly if it is emphasised that patients have to make a start to re-establish their careers.

For very disabled patients, it may not be realistic to expect them to be able to get back to work. Even for the less disabled, whether they can return to paid employment depends on the economic climate. It might be virtually impossible to get a job during a deep recession. In these circumstances, unpaid work will have to be considered. Furthermore, therapists might have to help families of very disabled patients to define 'work' broadly. Just as running a home can be defined as full-time employment, patients' contribution to the running of the home can be seen as 'work'. Sometimes, particularly in the marital home with the wife being employed full-time, the patient's contribution to running of the home can be seen as role reversal. Similarly, attendance at a day centre can be construed as work. In a relatives' group it is possible to share the problem of helping a patient back into some structured activities, despite negative symptoms. Therapists' and other relatives' recognition and encouragement of the effort involved is important to help relatives maintain any progress.

Clinical example
T1. Do you feel you've been quite successful in getting David up and to the hospital each day?
Mrs A. Well it has been successful, but I don't know if it served any good purpose. He's not gone to the hospital and done anything.
T2. Well it is good for him.
T1. It gets him into a bit of a routine.
Mrs B. [To Mrs A] You need to keep emphasising that.
T1. He's not just staying at home all day.

Summary

A behavioural approach to the performance of tasks at home by the patient gives the opportunity to exercise skills needed in a job. When applying for jobs, patients face the dilemma of how much to reveal of their psychiatric history. There is no clear-cut answer, but the therapists should discuss the pros and cons with the patient and the family. Families may need help in adjusting to the patient's impaired work skills and the reduced likelihood of finding open employment or returning to full-time studies. For the very disabled patients, families will have to be persuaded to accept alternatives such as helping out at home or attending a day centre.

22 Cultural issues

All large cities in Britain contain peoples of ethnic minorities who have migrated more or less recently. Some will have found it relatively easy to assimilate into the majority white culture. Others strongly maintain their culture of origin and resist pressures to assimilate. Therapists need to be aware of the range of cultures they are likely to come into contact with in their work with families, and must cultivate sensitivity to cultural issues that have a direct bearing on the work.

Language

This is the most obvious factor that may constitute an insuperable barrier to family work. If one of the key family members is able to speak English only poorly or not at all, the ideal solution is to find a therapist who can speak the family's language. Failing this, it is possible to use an interpreter in family sessions who is not a member of the family. However, this has the disadvantages of slowing down communication, and of inhibiting the family's responses because of the presence of a stranger whom they might not trust. For example, they could worry that the interpreter might meet them later in a social setting, which is quite likely if the ethnic community is small. The alternative of using family members as interpreters is also problematic, since they may have reservations about representing the opinions of someone they disagree with. Hence the therapists could be given a censored version. Since both these solutions have disadvantages, the therapists need to weigh one against the other to make a decision.

Even when the therapists speak the same non-English language as the family, there can be difficulties in translating the concepts used in this work from English to the other language. Therapists should be aware of this difficulty, and need to check the family's understanding of particular concepts by asking for feedback.

Ethnic matching of therapists with clients

Even if the family is fluent in English, it has been proposed by some that therapists should be chosen with a similar cultural background to that of the clients. In most services it is difficult to match therapists with recent immigrant groups because it takes some years for members of such groups to work their way onto and up the professional ladder. Even with well established ethnic minorities, there is unlikely to be sufficient flexibility in the service to consider ethnic matching because of a general shortage of staff and in particular of those from the relevant ethnic groups. The most practical solution is to ensure that all therapists are well versed in the cultural issues discussed in this chapter.

Family structure

The structure of the family in the majority white culture in Britain has changed dramatically over the past 100 years. Large extended families, which were common in the Victorian era, have shrunk to the nuclear family with two parents and two children. Even the nuclear family has been eroded, as currently 40% of marriages end in divorce and almost one in five families are headed by a single parent. Furthermore, 'blended' families, with children from different partners, are becoming more common.

As a result of divorce or death of the partner, it is common to find one elderly parent, almost always the mother, looking after a middle-aged schizophrenic patient by herself.

By contrast, many ethnic minority families retain a traditional structure, with large numbers of children and more distant relatives either sharing the household or, if not, being closely involved in their lives. Therapists must be prepared to hold family meetings with all adult members, including those in the extended family, since they may play an important role in supporting the patient.

In ethnic minorities, families are not only larger but usually are more hierarchical. The parents expect respect and a sense of duty from their children. These have all but vanished from white majority families, although some people can remember a time when sons addressed their fathers as 'Sir'. In some traditional families there are strict rules regulating communication. For instance, senior members must not converse with the most junior members except through an intermediary. Therapists should respect this structure, however different it is from their own experience. The children in traditional families will often have been caught up in a conflict between the values of their family and those of the white majority culture, to which they will usually have been exposed at school. Therapists may be tempted to side with the children against the parents, but this should be resisted. They should do their best to give equal support to members of both generations, recognising that such conflicts are inevitable and that there may be no obvious solution.

One aspect of stronger parental authority that may impinge on family work is the arranged marriage. Often such marriages are arranged through other parents, the prospective bride and groom not meeting until the wedding day. Sometimes traditional parents see this as the salvation for a son or daughter with schizophrenia, and the mental illness of one partner remains concealed throughout the negotiations. The therapists need to raise the issue that marriage can be harmful or beneficial to the patient, depending on the nature of the relationship with the spouse. This cannot easily be predicted from parental knowledge of the two partners, and is best determined by allowing them to spend some time together before the marriage is settled. However, therapists will often find themselves blocked by traditional values and customs.

The question of the appropriate age for children to become independent of their parents is also heavily influenced by culture. In traditional families, the children may be expected to stay with their parents throughout their life and support them in their old age. Therapists must make allowance for this in setting goals for increased independence of the schizophrenic patient.

The structure of Afro-Caribbean families may be different from that of white majority families because of the nature of their immigration. It was quite common for the younger children to be left in the West Indies with grandparents and to join their parents in Britain some years later, when they had established themselves economically. Sometimes, by the time they joined the family, the parents had divorced and there was a step-parent and step-siblings. These disruptions in family relationships can cause emotional disturbances, to which the therapists should be sensitive.

Another feature of Afro-Caribbean families is that sometimes the adult men are not permanently resident in the household, but come and go. This can be encountered with the husbands of schizophrenic women or the fathers of schizophrenic children. It can be difficult to engage in family work men who are transient in this way. Nevertheless, persistent efforts should be made to do so.

Maintaining 'face'

In traditional cultures, particularly in Asia, a great deal of importance is attached to maintaining the family's respect in the eyes of neighbours, distant relatives, and society in general. Mental illness is heavily stigmatised, and the thought that its presence in a family member could become public knowledge is likely to raise anxieties about 'losing face'. It can also be seen as a blight on the marriage prospects of other children in the family. Hence the therapists have to approach education of the family tactfully, and anticipate negative reactions to the diagnosis. It is likely to be more difficult to persuade relatives from traditional families to attend the relatives' group. Furthermore they may be reluctant for the patient to attend facilities outside the home.

The advantages

Despite these difficulties it is important to remember that the outcome for schizophrenia in Third World countries is considerably better than in the West, partly because of more tolerant attitudes of relatives. The extended family is a valuable resource for supporting schizophrenic patients. Rather than feeling overwhelmed by the large families of ethnic minority patients, therapists should view them as a network of potential allies.

Summary

Cultural issues arise regularly in therapeutic work in cities. Language barriers require the use of an interpreter, but this is problematic in family work. Therapists have to take account of the variation in family structure and roles across cultures. Mental illness is more heavily stigmatised in families from developing countries. Although ethnic matching of clients and therapists might be ideal, it is impractical. Therefore therapists need to develop a sensitivity to cultural issues.

23 Special problems complicating family work

Alcohol and substance abuse

The most common concerns with regard to substance abuse among families of schizophrenic patients are problems relating to alcohol, cigarettes, soft drugs such as marijuana, and excessive caffeine intake.

Clinical example
In this family alcohol and drug abuse were a problem.
T. Do you think you are less well now than you have been Leslie, if you couldn't sleep all night?
P. Well the Sudafed makes me, keeps me awake unless I've had a drink and taken some chlorpromazine.
T. You seem shaky today as well.
M. Then why do you take it? Is it meant to do you any good?
P. There's a drug in it which is speed. It gives me my anxiety totally away from my self-conscious so I don't call on my subconscious.

Drugs and substance abuse are often an emotional issue. The evidence that certain ethnic groups are more likely to use soft drugs is equivocal. However, it is a common misconception among some relatives that the patient's illness started because they mixed in bad company and used drugs, hence misattributing the cause of the illness entirely to drug abuse. While it is true that soft drugs or other recreational drugs have the unfortunate effect of enhancing vulnerability to the onset of the illness or relapses, drugs on their own do not cause the illness. This should be made clear to patients and their families, so that patients do not get blamed for causing their illness. However, the danger of using recreational drugs should be made clear to patients. We find it useful to have routine educational sessions about the danger of drug use while patients are still in hospital, and then to reiterate the harmful effects during family sessions if the use of recreational drugs is a problem. Patients should be advised clearly against any drug or substance abuse.

Alcohol is a common problem. Schizophrenic patients like visiting pubs where they can blend into an environment which provides some sort of social stimulation, without it being too demanding for them. Furthermore, visiting pubs is part of the culture for certain sections of the population in Britain. Patients may not feel one of the crowd, going to pubs with friends, if they abstain completely from alcohol. Unfortunately, alcohol does potentiate the sedative effects of tranquillisers. Patients should be warned about this as part of the educational process. A few patients become violent when demanding money for drinks or when drunk.

Complete abstinence may not be possible or necessary. Family members often worry about this and object to, or even try to take control of, the situation. This is unlikely to be successful without the patient's cooperation. As with any problems families have, patients' and relatives' concerns and points of view should be voiced in meetings. Patients and families should be helped to see the potential problems relating to alcohol intake and yet not lose sight of the opportunities to socialise with limited alcohol intake. Patients then should be helped to experiment with how much alcohol they can take without getting intoxicated. We often advise patients to order half pints rather than full pints when going out in a crowd. Low alcohol beer is a good alternative.

Clinical example
In this session the double problem of drug taking and drinking had been worked on.
T.   Last time we met we talked about how to organise the weekend. We compromised on Leslie going to stay with you on Friday and Sunday. I was just wondering how it's been?
M.   The last weekend sort of took care of itself because Leslie didn't come up till Saturday. He was very good; he didn't drink either night.
T.   Wonderful.
M.   I think he was a lot better for it.
T.   What did you say to Leslie when he didn't drink?
M.   I think I was just very pleased that he didn't get drunk. We set that arrangement and he stuck by it and I shall say it in the future, no coming home if he drinks, because it's not good for him and not good for me.
T.   How did you find the weekend Leslie?
P.   All right.
The therapists are also making sure that both sides join in, note the progress, and reinforce positive changes.

Cigarette smoking is another common concern, owing to hazards to physical health. Often the complaint is not the smoking as such but the danger of setting the house on fire when patients are smoking in bed, or untidiness associated with smoking. Patients often say they smoke because of boredom. The problem of physical dependence, the usual scenario of fellow patients smoking heavily, and cigarettes being a central focus for social interaction among patients make giving up smoking difficult. Often the solution is to help families to set limits with regard to specific problem behaviour relating to smoking. For example, the practice of smoking in bed should be discouraged, particularly if the patient is taking large doses of tranquillisers. Limits should also be set with regard to the use and emptying of ashtrays if that is a problem.

Lastly, some patients drink an enormous amount of tea or coffee. This can lead to shakiness, nervousness, excitement, restlessness, and sleep problems. It should be explained to patients that sometimes it is difficult to separate the effects of too much caffeine intake from anxiety or the schizophrenic process itself. The amount of caffeine intake should, therefore, be moderated.

Incest, child abuse

This does not occur more frequently in families where one member suffers from schizophrenia, as far as we know, but during family work it is likely that an occasional family will have this as an additional problem.

The important issue here, as with alcohol and substance abuse, is to separate the family problems caused by the illness from those caused by the abuse. If the abuse is in the past, this will be one of the main tasks of the family work.

If the abuse is current or not previously discovered, then other agencies should be called in, in the same way that therapists would with any family. Child abuse is a serious offence; evidence that it is occurring would have to be taken further, and children involved protected as far as possible. If this happens then the family are bound to feel ambivalent about the therapists, and it may not be possible to continue working with them. Even if work continues, the impact of calling in outside agencies will have to be discussed with the family.

Any 'secret', and sexual abuse is one of the most likely, causes a conflict of interest for therapists. If therapists are told a 'secret' that others in the family may not share, then it makes family work more difficult. We have often found that the 'secret' is known, but that family members are not able to talk to each other about it. Apart from sexual abuse (when therapists have to act on the knowledge, despite issues of confidentiality and trust), the aim with most 'secrets' is to enable the confiding family member to discuss it more openly in a family meeting. If therapists can give support for this, often all family members will feel relief at the subject finally being aired.

In our experience, when child abuse has been a problem, the damage done to the marital and child relationships as a result considerably complicates the problems of schizophrenia, and are particularly difficult to repair.

Suicide

In a condition such as schizophrenia the risk of suicide, both threatened and successful, is high, and most patients and families will have some experience of this. The lifetime risk among patients is 10%. Some families react by becoming excessively cautious and overprotective. Others will not believe that the patient is serious and may underestimate the risks. If a relationship is particularly poor, or the relatives particularly burdened, relatives may even wish that the patient were dead – we have heard this said both in a relatives' group and in front of the patient during a family meeting.

If this happens, therapists have to interrupt the meeting and immediately comment on and reframe the remarks. We have found that even brutal-sounding statements like these can be looked at positively. They are also quite likely to have been said before, and are probably less shocking to other family members than to therapists. In this particular example, in the family meeting it was possible for therapists to comment on the fact that a relative felt like this because of concern that the patient's quality of life was so poor that she would be better off dead. The patient was then able to reassure the relative about it and appreciate the concern. In a relatives' group, several relatives admitted wishing the patient dead, and similar reasons were elicited – that is, fears that patients' lives now were almost unbearable. Once voiced, it was possible for relatives to discuss with and reassure each other that there were still positive aspects about the patients they lived with.

It is helpful to establish with the family and the patient the reality of suicidal feelings, and possible actions. Patients may well have warning signs of these feelings – either as part of a relapse, or as part of new feelings of depression. Often, as positive symptoms of schizophrenia decrease, and the patient returns to some appreciation of reality, they may also be faced with severe feelings of loss and hopelessness – that they will never recover fully, and that life will always be more difficult from now on. If a patient can share such feelings and possible warning signs, or relatives are familiar with them, then the action that can and should be taken can be rehearsed with the family. If it is possible to do this before a crisis arises, it will help to defuse the anxiety of a real crisis and enable relatively quick action to be taken. Depending on the local services, it may be helpful to suggest a telephone call to the general practitioner, the team, or the emergency services if the family or the patient are very concerned.

If patients become depressed or hopeless, they may need individual help. It may be necessary to discuss the fact of lowered expectations and help them come to terms with it. A useful technique is 'collapsing time' (mentioned in Chapter 7), to discuss how they can make progress in a very long time span such as one or two years – it may be possible to look back over previous years to find evidence of this. For example, "Do you remember five years ago, when you were always in hospital?"

A successful suicide is a devastating event if therapists are working with the family at the time. Relatives will feel considerable anger and, of course, be extremely upset. Often relatives will feel somebody is to blame. Normally there will be a hospital inquiry, an inquest, and possibly court proceedings. Not all suicides are preventable, and therapists need to remember this. Normally, staff and relatives will have tried to prevent the death, and this will have been documented. On the other hand all involved will feel guilty and upset that prevention was not possible for whatever reason. Therapists will be likely to be upset and shaken themselves. They may also feel anger and resentment at the patient for causing such upset.

These situations are difficult to deal with. It helps if therapists are as open and understanding as possible with relatives, even if the family are angry. It can defuse things if therapists can say that they too are shocked and sad. Some families require contact and want to meet to discuss what happened; others will cut off and not want to have to deal with 'psychiatric staff' any more. The family's wishes have to be respected. We have found that if no other contact is wanted, a short letter of sympathy can still be helpful.

Similar principles apply if the death is not suicide but due to some other cause. Therapists will be upset, and the family is unlikely to want to continue contact. Again, a short letter of sympathy can be helpful and may be easier to manage than a telephone call.

The family's permission must be sought if staff wish to attend the funeral.

The offer of continuing sessions or attendance at a relatives' group should be made, but may not be taken up. In a relatives' group, a death needs to be discussed openly with group members, and will obviously raise fears of vulnerability, and what may happen in the future for members.

Physical disabilities

It is quite common in long-term mental illness to find that patients (or relatives) have physical disabilities that complicate the problems of schizophrenia. Sometimes physical problems predate the illness, so that the patient has always had to have special care or help, and this can mark the start of an overinvolved relationship with a parent. Sometimes physical difficulties start at the same time as schizophrenia. For some patients physical problems arise because of damage done during suicide attempts. Others have physical problems that arise later.

The aim here is to separate out the problem due to physical needs, and those due to mental illness. Both patient and family may not understand the difference and may over- or underprotect the patient as a result.

Once in the 'invalid' role, patients may not wish to be independent and may lose confidence in the abilities that remain. One patient who needed lengthy physical treatment lost all community skills because of being 'looked after' in a general hospital, and had to be encouraged over many months to go out of the house again.

Often physical treatments, for example for diabetes, continue alongside treatment for mental health. Being involved in two teams can lead to confusion, and therapists should be able to liaise with the other team and act as advocates for the patient and relatives if necessary. Patients with mental health problems which include negative symptoms can have serious motivational problems in taking long-term treatment for physical problems, and in attending clinics. This can be discussed in the family meetings and then dealt with as other problems would be.

More than one person in the family with schizophrenia

This is not common, but we have come across and worked with such families. Most typically, both partners in a marriage meet in hospital, and although it is likely that one is better, and is actually the carer, therapists may find that there is not a 'well' relative to deal with in family sessions. We have also met families where a parent and a child have schizophrenia, and other families where more than one child is ill.

Usually in these situations, only one person is the 'patient' for the therapists, and other family members will be seen by other teams. Sometimes however it will be seen as sensible for both relatives to be 'patients'. This can lead to a conflict of interest for therapists, and to the patients feeling that only one of them (the more needy one) is getting help. Therapists need to be aware of this, to make sure both parties feel attended to equally.

Another problem that can arise is the fact that because schizophrenia is a diverse condition, one person in the family may have the diagnosis and yet have a very different pattern from the other. This leads to confusion for both patients and relatives, with comments such as "I've managed to cope with my voices; why can't you?" The different severities of schizophrenia and even the possibility of different treatment regimes need to be explained by therapists, and help given according to what the problems are at that time. Occasionally the better 'patient' can be used as an ally to help the worse one, but often they are rather resentful of the attention given, and a positive response cannot be relied upon. Well members of the family, if they exist (and it may be necessary to involve the whole network), are particularly important to include and mobilise in family meetings in order to encourage healthy behaviour rather than problems. Sometimes a previously undiagnosed family member will volunteer psychotic symptoms and their own coping responses. It can be reassuring for patients to know that they are not unique in having strange experiences. However, although personally successful, the suggested solutions are often idiosyncratic and may not be helpful or acceptable to the patient. Therapists should take such suggestions seriously and allow them to be discussed, but establish that patients have to make their own decisions and may not share identical problems with other family members.

Working with several other agencies

As has been mentioned, some families are involved with more than one team. Sometimes this is because there are multiple problems in the family, as discussed under physical problems; sometimes families attract multi-agency input because they are demanding of or are dissatisfied with services.

Therapists in this situation should be aware that the opportunities for misinformation, splitting, and an uncoordinated approach multiply with the number of agencies. It is worth remembering that if a family complains of the 'other' team to therapists they may be equally dissatisfied with family meetings. It is sensible to check directly with the other agency what their viewpoint is, or what their aims are with the family, rather than just accepting the family view.

If possible, one agency should provide the major input to a family and other agencies should channel through and liaise with them. If other therapists are already doing some family work, it would not be sensible to start sessions with the family as well, and some discussion should take place as to which therapists are going to continue, and who should withdraw. The potential for sabotage and confusion makes it too difficult to offer family work in 'competition' with another agency.

Another possibility is that therapists discover the involvement of another agency only after several sessions – the family omit to mention it at first. Again, therapists need to talk to the other workers directly and negotiate with the most appropriate contact.

Families who reject therapists

It does happen that despite families being well engaged with meetings and attending, sometimes for months, therapists are told not to come again. This will feel rejecting for the therapists, who may also be quite shocked and angry at the family for making such a sudden decision. They have to accept what the family says, but if at all possible try to find out what the problem is. If it is something specific it may be possible for therapists to change their approach or deal with the problem and all may be well. However, some families become adamant at being questioned and the situation may not improve. If this is the case, therapists should try to negotiate a 'final session' in order to say goodbye and to do some work on leaving. Even if both sides are quite upset and angry, a final session, arranged for a few weeks' time, will allow for a cooling off period. This in itself may encourage a different perspective by the next visit. If the family is still adamant, however, therapists should aim to be constructive in the 'goodbye' session. Progress should be reviewed, and coping strategies rehearsed for any emergencies that might arise. Therapists should leave open the possibility that they can be contacted (e.g. leaving a telephone number) even if this is rejected by the family at the time. It is important for therapists not to show that they are too perturbed by the family behaviour. They should say that they would like to see the family again if they change their mind, and wish them well for the future. Often this 'lifeline' will in fact be used. Another strategy is for therapists themselves to telephone 'for a chat' in a few weeks' time. This establishes that therapists themselves are still willing to be involved and are still concerned, and can allow a reappraisal of any current problems.

Being rejected by the family will not feel comfortable for the therapists and they should talk it over together. We have found when it does happen the reason is likely to be that the family find change too difficult at that time, and so end the sessions to protect themselves.

Summary

It is not uncommon to find that families are not just coping with schizophrenia, but are also facing a range of other problems which may cause as much or even more concern. These include alcohol or substance abuse, child abuse, suicide attempts, physical disabilities, and more than one family member with schizophrenia. Where there are multiple problems, the therapists need to help the family sort out the issues involved and deal with them adequately. Families sometimes reject the help offered. When this happens it is important for the therapists to offer them the possibility of future contact.

24 Running a relatives' group. I

We recommend that, where possible, therapists set up a relatives' group that runs in parallel with the family sessions. However, we recognise that in some settings it will be impractical to do both. In these instances the advantages and disadvantages of groups as opposed to family sessions should be weighed up in order to make a choice.

Advantages of relatives' groups

(a) We know from our research that relatives' groups can be as effective as family sessions in helping families to cope better with problems and in reducing patients' relapse rate (Leff *et al*, 1989, 1990).

(b) Relatives' groups are cost-effective. Two therapists can work with 10 to 12 relatives in one group.

(c) They provide a good forum to express and process feelings, especially negative ones that would upset patients if exposed to them.

(d) The presence of other relatives creates the social pressure of a peer group who understand the problems. Furthermore relatives (compared with professionals) can be very frank and forceful with each other without causing offence.

(e) A wider variety of solutions to difficult problems are likely to be proposed by a group than by a family, which may contain only a single relative.

(f) Groups expand relatives' social networks, which are often reduced by living with schizophrenia. They help to relieve the resultant isolation and feelings of guilt and stigma.

(g) Because relatives are likely to be living with patients in different stages of the illness, a group offers hope for survival to 'newer' relatives.

Disadvantages of relatives' groups

(a) A group does not allow therapists to observe interaction between patients and relatives, which can deepen the therapists' understanding of the problems.

(b) Therapists only get to hear one viewpoint – the relatives'.

(c) A group cannot deal with worries that relatives feel are too private or intimate to be aired, such as marital or sexual problems.

(d) 'Newer' relatives may be upset by meeting relatives with very long-term problems.

(e) Some relatives will not attend a group, so that by itself a group will fail to offer a service to *all* families. In particular those difficult to engage, the infirm or disabled, the elderly, and relatives who cannot manage the time of the meeting will be neglected. Our research has shown that patients have a poor outcome in families who are offered the group but fail to attend (Leff *et al*, 1989).

General issues

One of the main features distinguishing relatives' groups from the family work described previously is that patients are not involved. This has been done deliberately in order that relatives feel unconstrained enough to discuss a range of emotional aspects with other people in the group. Relatives are relieved by this and we have found it works well.

Clinical example
This discussion is about the possibility of a relapse.
T. You're hoping it's going to be alright in the future Mr A, because as you say last time it was a 'nightmare' for you.
Mr A. Oh if it happens again I'm off, I'm going, I'll ring up Dr T and say "I'm bailing out".
Mrs B. I can understand that, because we went through hell.

A relatives' group immediately creates a problem in that patients may feel excluded, and some will be suspicious and upset at the prospect of relatives attending a separate meeting. We have found that saying the following to patients will reassure all but the most paranoid.

(a) that relatives themselves need help

(b) that it is useful to meet with others who understand the problem

(c) that we are not discussing the patients so much as trying to ensure that relatives cope better.

Clinical example
In one relatives' group they discuss how to cope with a patient's worries about what is said in a meeting.

T. What do you say to your husband?

Mrs Y. Everything. Absolutely.

Mr X. [To Mrs Y] Do you think I ought to go home and tell my wife?

Mrs Y. She's obviously feeling a bit left out, even though she's the cause of it, perhaps even jealous that you belong to a group. One way round it is to let her know you've been helped a lot by hearing other people's experiences. You could say, "A lot of them are like you dear, but it's just nice to hear other people talking about someone ill with them." You could describe to her what some of us are like.

Mr X. I find being cross-examined about what happened here embarrassing.

Mrs Y. You needn't say anything about what you said. She might feel more included if you tell her about us. Let's say you go home and I'm you. And you say "There's a new girl there today, because her husband's been admitted really psychotic," maybe she might feel. . .

Mrs Z. Better about it, not extraordinary.

Another feature of relatives' groups is that therapists have to work particularly hard to persuade people to attend. Unlike meetings in the home, relatives' groups must be held somewhere central, and this means that everybody has to travel. Since many relatives are elderly, some may be disabled or unwell, some may be in employment, there is always a problem of motivation and often a problem over timing – for example an evening group will suit those in work but not those who are elderly or infirm and dislike going out at night. It is also difficult to engage people in a new venture which requires meeting unknown people to discuss issues that were previously felt to be private and perhaps stigmatised. We have found that between a quarter and a half of potential relatives will not attend a group even when offered lifts and sent letters reminding them of each meeting. Although, as mentioned above, it is cost-effective and can produce results as good as seeing families at home, it will always be the case that not all families will attend. These families will need sessions at home, since therapists on a doorstep are hard to refuse, whereas going out on a winter evening is easily avoided.

In order to maximise engagement we recommend that if possible therapists should meet relatives before a group is set up. Often this can be done by giving relatives the education package at home. It is less daunting to attend a group if relatives at least know the therapist.

Venue

Ideally a venue should be convenient, accessible, already known to the relatives and welcoming. There may be an argument for taking the group away from a mental health setting and organising it in a local community centre; however, this is likely to work only if relatives are already used to attending there for some other reason. Some relatives have suggested holding the group in a building close to shops and other facilities such as a pub. The room used should be comfortable, large enough to manage up to, say, 15 people, but not so huge as to be intimidating. We have always run groups that included refreshments, so access to a kitchen and tea-making facilities are essential. The latter emphasises the social as well as the emotional needs of carers, and helps members to feel relaxed. As increasing the social network is likely to be an aim of a relatives' group, this aspect is more important than it may seem.

Timing

As mentioned earlier, timing is not likely to suit everyone and should be negotiated if at all possible. We have usually held groups in the afternoon or early evenings; the former suits the elderly and retired, the latter those in work. The groups normally last for an hour and a half and are typically run once a fortnight, particularly if most families are at the beginning of the illness. For families of very long-term patients, we have found that once a month is a better frequency as new issues are less likely to arise.

Selection

Our main criteria for selection would be that all group members share a patient with the same diagnosis, that is, schizophrenia. If different diagnoses are included, patients' problems are not similar enough and it is difficult for the group members to develop themes and to feel that others understand their difficulties. The more similar members are, the easier it will be to develop common strategies that they will accept from each other. Most relatives will be parents, some will be spouses, others will be siblings or children. If there are at least two of each sort it will help the group to feel that they share experiences; if this is not possible the therapists will have to work harder to make sure that the only spouse or only father does not feel marginalised.

The only other aspect that we ensure is that all relatives have received the education (see Chapter 5) before the group starts. This gives each relative a common base, and it means that one of the therapists is likely to have met the relatives already. Giving the education first also means that therapists have already provided something for relatives – information that was asked for – and so increases relatives' motivation to attend subsequently.

Size

If there are more than 12 people in the group, it will be difficult to attend to and give support for everyone's needs. Too few people will mean that the group is hardly viable; therapists are effectively holding individual sessions.

Open or closed groups?

We have always run an open group, mainly because of the difficulties of recruiting. Thus, relatives can start a group, continue it, preferably for about nine months, and then leave, while being replaced by other members. This has the advantage of new members introducing variety. It also allows relatives at different stages in the illness to join a group and see for themselves that even very difficult problems can be coped with and survived. However, the relatives of first-onset patients can find listening to long-term problems discouraging, and they will need extra support in the group, and sometimes outside it, to deal with this. There is an argument for seeing all relatives of first-onset patients in a separate group, but it is unusual to find enough people at the same time to make this practical.

Aims of a relatives' group

These are:

(a) to help lower criticism and overinvolvement in relatives
(b) to help relatives share experiences and process the emotional upset that they have had
(c) to allow relatives to pool solutions to problems and help each other to try out new ways of coping with common difficulties
(d) to increase relatives' social network to combat feelings of isolation and stigma.

These aims are achieved by encouraging relatives to talk to each other about their experiences, to share and thus normalise the emotional impact, and to allow relatives to solve common problems and try out new ways of coping.

Therapists' role

Although this is a group, the methods used by the therapists do not rely on traditional or psychodynamic 'group processes'. The therapists' role is to facilitate the group members' interaction in order to allow them to achieve the above aims. Thus, many of the same tactics used with families are also required in the group. Relatives must 'take turns', listen to each other, and not all talk at once. The atmosphere of the group must be friendly and positive while also allowing serious issues to be tackled and problems solved. Relatives' groups are particularly good at dealing with the emotional processing that families may not have managed previously. Group members must be able to trust each other and the therapists enough to raise these issues. Upsetting emotions must be allowed, normalised, and used positively. The group must therefore be safe enough to enable this. Therapists must also take control and be directive enough to help members stick with one subject and manage to talk about an issue so that there is some productive conclusion. Otherwise the members can avoid discussion of problems and the time spent together will not help families to change their behaviour.

Summary

A relatives' group is desirable but may not always be practical to set up. If it is established, a relatives' group requires similar skills to those discussed in the family sessions; the aims and methods are parallel. Therapists are primarily facilitators. Relatives need help to engage in the group, and patients may be suspicious of its purpose. The venue should be convenient, and kitchen facilities should be available.

25 Running a relatives' group. II

The first group meeting

It is important for the first meeting to help everyone to relax and to begin to get to know each other. Everyone should be welcomed and the therapists introduce themselves as relatives arrive. In our experience, a good way to start the meeting is to ask every relative to give a short version of their 'story', that is, their name, the patient's name, and an account of what has happened to them since the illness began. Asking each relative to do this for themselves allows them to keep control of the story and to reveal only what they feel comfortable with. Even so, some relatives may need encouragement to talk at all, and the therapists should provide this. Relatives should be asked to talk in turn, and therapists should ensure that they are listened to and not interrupted. This emphasises that in the group turn-taking and listening are important, in the same way as they are in the family sessions. If one relative or one couple tells a very involved story and begins to dominate the meeting, the therapists should interrupt politely and say that the meeting will return to their problems later on or in a subsequent meeting; it is important that therapists establish from the start that everyone in the room should be given the chance to contribute.

As relatives begin to talk about their experiences, the group will begin to discover the similarities between them. Therapists should also emphasise these as they occur – "You just mentioned that, didn't you Mrs X?" or "You felt like that too." This not only begins the process of 'communality' that is an important feature of these relatives' groups, but also makes the point that therapists have been listening and are able to draw out the themes.

The main aim of the first meeting is to establish how much all the participants share in common, despite differences in background or

101

relationship. Any relative with some uncommon feature must be reassured by the therapists that their problem is not particularly unusual even if no one else in the group mentions it, otherwise they will feel isolated and it will be harder for them to attend next time. Therapists should ensure that everyone has a chance to participate and that each person's contribution is valued. After the 'stories' have been heard, some aspect that several relatives have experience of should be focused on. This allows a discussion to develop, and therapists should ask for everyone's view. It is important that therapists keep control during this sort of discussion, as it cannot be assumed that relatives will all have the same level of social and participatory skills. It will often be necessary to reinforce listening to each other, to emphasise that relatives must not interrupt too often, and to make sure that only one person talks at a time. This latter can be introduced as a 'rule' of the group; otherwise it is easy for relatives to try to have parallel conversations, either with each other or with each therapist, and the group will become chaotic.

We have found that having a break for tea and biscuits in the middle of the meeting works well. It allows relatives to enjoy the social side of a group, it helps people to relax, and it emphasises that the group shares some of the characteristics of other meetings that they may have attended. Once the tea is served, however, we carry on with the meeting.

Subsequent meetings

After the first meeting, it is important that the therapists should continue to have clear aims for each meeting and should impose some structure, otherwise the group will soon feel repetitious and pointless. We would usually begin each subsequent meeting with an open inquiry to each relative as to how things had been since the last time. This allows any urgent or unexpected events to be raised and looked at by the group. Any new group members should be introduced in the same way as in the first meeting – all group members can be asked for their 'story'. The new member is included in this exercise, although not necessarily asked to begin it, and this helps not only to introduce everybody but also allows the new person to join the group.

During each meeting the therapist should be alert to any theme or common problem that is being mentioned. Part of the point of each meeting is to allow group members to focus on common issues that they probably previously thought were quite individual. This allows members not only a chance to 'normalise' their difficulties, but, even more important, to use the group to find and then try out some new ways of coping. Thus once an issue has been identified and agreed on with the group, the therapists' role is to enable members to discuss it in some depth, to stay with one problem and not stray off the point, and, finally, to come to some low-EE consensus as to a possible solution. This can be extremely difficult to achieve if all group members have high-EE ratings, and this is one of the reasons we suggest having two therapists. Another strategy is to try to ensure that at least some low-EE relatives attend the group. They will be harder to engage, as their needs will be different, but if they do join the group, therapists can use their experiences of coping with problems as a realistic but alternative model. Low-EE relatives can be a asset in group because they have had to cope with the same difficulties, and have often found a more effective coping strategy.

Clinical example
Mrs A was very angry with her husband's demanding and irritable behaviour.

Mrs A. It's part of this illness. They've got us there and there's nothing we can do about it. It sounds half the time that we let them have their own way; we do, but it's just to live in the same house with them. That's what it boils down to: we've got to live with these people and it doesn't matter how bitter and hurt you're feeling, we've got to tolerate their way of carrying on. Haven't you found that?

Mrs B. Up to a point.

Mrs A. Half the time you can say what's your bloody game, why did you do this?

Mrs B. I think acceptance is the great thing. What they say to you; you know damn well they're trying to irritate you or doing something like that.

Mrs A. This is it.

Mrs B. And you just have to let it ride.

Mrs A. It's what you do eight out of ten times. It just seems so bloody unfair.

Mrs B. You've got to do that, otherwise you'll always be at loggerheads. You have to let it ride really if you can possibly do it.

T. What do you think Mr C?

Mr C. I normally go out.

Mr B. Don't give any back-chat.

Mr C. I have done, but over the years I've learnt that it doesn't avail anything at all, only upset myself. I just tolerate it now. If I talk to friends I can say what I like, because I know the person, but sometimes with my wife I have to think what I'm saying because she is hypersensitive and can take things to heart.

Mrs B. That's right.

Mr C. Things that wouldn't upset anyone else.

Themes

In early meetings of the group, while people are getting to know each other, most of the themes raised are likely to be practical. Relatives often ask a lot of questions, both of the therapist and of each other, which are usually a continuation of the education session. Issues raised include medication, the causes of schizophrenia, employment, problems with benefits, and practical problems caused by the patient. We recommend answering any questions as they arise, and at all times throwing questions open to the whole group to elicit their answers. In most groups therapists will find that at least one relative will have had experience of the problem and will be likely to have a useful opinion. Part of the value of a relatives' group is that it is easier to listen to the opinions and advice of someone who has had the same experience, and it is also deeply reassuring to hear that someone else has coped with or learnt to live with very difficult and intractable problems.

Later on, as more trust develops between group members, more difficult emotional issues will be raised. Groups provide a setting to deal with these: there are no patients present, so relatives feel they need not be constrained, and even negative emotions will have been felt by other group members. Typical issues will include the stigma of mental illness, feelings of isolation, grief, loss, and bereavement. Relatives will often feel angry and may want to reject the patient or the caring role. The power of the patient to make relatives feel guilty, helpless or frightened may be raised. Other emotional themes are the vulnerability of patients and relatives' fear of the future – 'Who will look after the patient when I am gone?' Finally, there will always be issues about services – how they have failed relatives, both in the past and currently. This may include the therapists' services, and should be dealt with calmly. It may be necessary to offer to act as an advocate to improve services, and this should be considered. Something as simple as a telephone call by a therapist may make an appreciable difference to the way a family is being dealt with.

Problem solving

As in the family sessions, if a problem is raised, attempts should be made during the group to solve it. It may be that several problems are mentioned at the beginning of the meeting, and then the therapists should attempt to prioritise them with the group members. Less urgent issues can always be deferred to a future meeting. Once a problem has been identified, possible solutions should be canvassed and discussed. Even reticent members should be asked for their views and encouraged to participate. The problem should be specified and broken into small, achievable bits, and the mechanics of any solutions should be discussed with the group in detail. If possible a task should be agreed on and homework set, to be reported on next time. Any progress that is achieved can then be powerfully reinforced by the whole group at the next meeting.

Clinical example
A patient's needs for reassurance had been discussed earlier, and the relatives' new response is reinforced by the group.
Mrs A. Eve makes excuses to go to bed. She won't go up unless someone is there. I can't explain it.
T1. What do you do now to reassure her?
Mr A. Usually I say I'm going; I don't force her to go to bed now. I say we're going to bed.
T1. So you leave her downstairs.
T2. Quite right.
Mrs A. I did once or twice creep down, but now she switches it all off herself.
Mrs B. That's good.

Sometimes, relatives get into a 'catch-22' of being unable to try a new solution. 'The problem is too difficult to have a solution, I have tried everything, any new solution could not work (because it would mean that I am a failure), therefore there is no solution.' Throughout the whole of the meeting they may argue this. Therapists should recognise this as a relative trying to avoid the uncertainty of change, and be reassuring. We have often found that relatives who do this will in fact manage a change between sessions, and be able to report back about it with enthusiasm next time.

Emotional processing

When relatives do begin to express emotional issues, particularly the negative ones, it is important that therapists are able to cope. By being aired, the emotions are shared with the rest of the group, and this allows them to be normalised and put in context. Even extreme emotions will have been experienced by other group members, and others in the group will also be likely to have come to terms with them, or at least have started the process. Therapists should use the group's experience in a positive way to show how even very upsetting and difficult feelings can lead to new ways of coping with and understanding problems. Therapists should also not be visibly shocked, even by very negative emotions, for instance wishing that a suicide attempt had been successful; by allowing them to be expressed in the safety of the group setting, they are helping to defuse them and reduce the likelihood of their being said to the patient. The burden of care can be shared in a group.

Clinical example
Mrs A. I get very tired. I feel like walking out of the house and not coming back.
T1. Why can't you do that, go for a walk but come back later?
Mrs A. Because I can't. Because of the roads. I've got that problem as well.
Mrs B. Have a long bath.

T1. Haven't you got a neighbour you could go to?
T2. It sounds as though you shut yourself away somewhere else.
Mrs A. I just get depressed.
Mrs C. I hide it from my daughter. I don't let her see I'm upset.
Mrs D. You couldn't hide it from Diane.
T2. If it makes you cry like that, perhaps you ought to let her know, later on, that is when you feel calmer; have a talk about how difficult it is.

Maintaining attendance

If group attendance falls, relatives who do turn up will begin to feel dispirited, and the group will become non-viable. Therapists can maintain attendance by being consistent themselves, by being positive and encouraging to those who do attend, by reminding each relative by letter of the date of each meeting, and, if necessary, by offering lifts to those relatives who are elderly or infirm.

Ending a group

Not all groups have an end. Some members may want to continue without a facilitator; sometimes therapists are able and willing to continue to run it. We have usually run a group for about two years. If it is going to end, it is important to give relatives plenty of warning, and to discuss with them what support they would like in the future. Sometimes relatives have become friendly enough with each other to feel that they will not need extra help – we have had relatives who have been to each other's homes, given each other lifts, and telephoned each other. Sometimes a therapist's telephone number will be seen as sufficient contact. One group wanted meetings that were less frequent, but included the patient – we provided six-weekly meetings for these relatives, who had not previously experienced family meetings. As a general issue, if no family sessions have been offered, because a relatives' group was the only facility, then individual sessions can be considered when the group ends.

Summary

Group meetings need structure and control if the necessary work of problem solving and emotional processing is to take place. Therapists must provide a warm, positive atmosphere, and be prepared to take active steps to maintain attendance. A range of issues will be discussed, initially practical ones and later more emotional ones.

26 Conclusion

We have conducted two clinical trials which demonstrated the effectiveness of our model of family work in schizophrenia. Furthermore, we have completed two pilot studies of training nurses and other paramedical professionals to work with families. The preliminary findings of our pilot studies are encouraging. Trainees learnt significantly more about schizophrenia and demonstrated a significant shift in attitudes and assumptions in the desired direction. It is important to determine whether trainee therapists will have a similar impact on families as researchers did in the two clinical trials. A second-generation clinical trial is planned that consists of training of therapists, evaluation of the trainees' acquisition of skills, and the effect of therapy on the families.

An important part of an intervention is for therapists to receive feedback from families. We achieve this by requesting each family member to fill in a Helpful Aspects of Therapy (HAT) form after each session (Appendix 2). This enables therapists to shape their practice in the light of how it is perceived by both relatives and patients. Problems that arise can be picked up early, hopefully allowing action to be taken to prevent therapy being refused.

The written feedback from family members has been encouraging and, as usual, instructive. We provide a sample of these comments to give a flavour of what it is like to work with families. Comments on family education and early sessions of therapy were on the whole positive. Trainee therapists were able to instil hope and set up good working relationships with families.

Effect of education

"Therapists explained the best way to support someone after a breakdown."
"It describes my background." (A patient)

"The discussion I found most helpful was learning why my daughter was feeling stiff sometimes and very weak. I know what to expect."

Effect of family sessions

"Helpful talking about housework, how my wife is going to carry out the task because she doesn't seem to concentrate on quite a lot of things."

"I feel it was helpful inasmuch as I was able to convey my feelings, and circumstances that are happening at this moment, and have been happening for a very long time." (A mother)

"Monitor reasons that may or may not account for my drinking and future support." (A patient)

"My own assertiveness. Trying to see both sides, which is more healthy. Being more flexible." (A patient)

"Finding out what upset my son the most, which is a great help to me."

"At the end of the meeting, my son [patient] apologised for being rude earlier and therefore was aware of the need to be nice again."

"Helpful hints for my own social activities." (A relative)

"Opening up my mother's emotional blackmail." (A patient)

Since in the HAT form we also asked for unhelpful aspects of therapy, therapists were able to obtain regular feedback from families on how they thought therapy was going. We found comments on unhelpful aspects of therapy just as important. Therapists could then deal with any confusion, unmet expectations or dissatisfaction with therapy in an early stage. Examples of comments are:

"I think this meeting is very important. We talked about my going into a hostel. Well, I am confused about that. I think some more care and understanding are needed." (A patient)

"I did not like the part that was uncaring, e.g. the warnings. And all that the way the therapists shouted at me. That wasn't very nice, was it?" (*perception* of a patient)

"My son [patient] seems content to go along as at present and his positive thinking has not so far led to any positive action."

"My daughter [patient] does not want to discuss her problems in front of her sisters because she did not come out of school with 'O' levels, feeling inferior."

"I feel perhaps more could have been achieved if I had been alone." (An emotionally overinvolved parent)

Sometimes what happened in sessions can be construed in very different ways by different family members. They are extremely informative for therapists. The following are some examples.

(a) After an early session with a family

"Meeting was not such a good idea because my sister seemed nervous knowing we are discussing her. It is an invasion of family privacy even though the meeting helps the doctors." (One sister)

"I think it was a good idea that the whole family were meeting and discussing our sister's illness in the comfort of our own home. For the first time I realised that I didn't really know what she was suffering from, but it's now much clearer to me. Beforehand the word 'schizophrenia' meant something totally different to me." (Another sister)

"Other sisters think she [patient] is lazy. Perhaps it is a good idea to have only me in the meeting." (The mother)

(b) After a session in which the importance of the carers' opportunity to take a break and care for themselves was discussed

"The suggestion of going out to provide a break for myself and my parents is unhelpful." (The patient)

"Therapists suggested that I have a weekend off or away from home, which I agree with. I hope my son will help his self-cooking and cleaning up after him."

Appendix 1. Education booklet

Schizophrenia: some notes for relatives about its effects, cause and treatment

These notes are an attempt to give you some information about schizophrenia, its effects, causes and treatment. In addition to the help and advice of your family doctor, community psychiatric nurses, social worker, psychologist or psychiatrist, you may find it helpful to contact the National Schizophrenia Fellowship.

We will try to describe what it is that has happened to your relative and what it is called.

In the past you may have found that your relative is not their usual self, that they do not talk to you like they used to, that they may prefer to spend time alone or that they see and hear things which you cannot. You may also have found that if you try to talk to them about it, you cannot persuade them that these things are not true.

You have probably asked yourselves, what is the matter? Is it serious? What happens now? You may have found out some of the answers already, but you may not know how they apply to a member of your own family. We hope these notes will help to answer some of these questions.

The things that may have worried you are the signs of a well recognised illness. We now know quite a lot about it. For example, we know that sometimes the person can hear and see things which are not there. Thinking can get muddled so that it can mean that the person loses touch with what is really happening and then things he or she says or does can look odd or unusual. Also, their feelings may change, they may become more intense so that your relative appears very miserable or very excited, or they may diminish so that he or she loses interest or shows less affection.

People who have these sorts of experiences suffer from a form of what is called schizophrenia. Schizophrenia is an illness. If affects people in different ways. The difficulty is that the sort of experiences it gives rise to seem completely real to the people suffering from it but are hard to explain. For instance, someone who hears voices may talk back to them because they think they are voices of people who are actually there. Someone who seems to be very cold may not be able to be friendly because their feelings have been swamped by the illness. Someone who is very awkward or does not want to do ordinary things like the rest of the family may be like that because the illness has made them completely wrapped up in themselves and they do not realise or care that they are upsetting others.

Because the person cannot usually explain what is happening it is not always easy for other people, even those who live with them like yourselves, to realise that many of the odd or upsetting things he or she does are caused by the illness. It is especially hard because it is a mental and not a physical illness, so there are no outward signs of anything being wrong. For example, it is much easier to understand why someone with rheumatism can't do so much around the house, or perhaps can't get to work, than it is to understand why someone with schizophrenia may not be able to do these things.

Schizophrenia is not a rare illness. One out of every hundred people will probably suffer from it during their lifetime.

It can affect anyone. It is an illness that starts mainly in young people in their twenties, when most people are getting married or moving out of home. Both men and women can suffer from it, although it tends to start some years earlier in men. Schizophrenia also occurs all over the world: it is not something that just affects people in Britain.

Symptoms

Now we would like to go into more detail about the sort of things that can happen to someone who has schizophrenia. Individuals suffering from schizophrenia can have very different experiences. However certain things happen to almost everyone at some stage of the illness.

Disturbances of thinking are very common. You may have noticed that sometimes your relative says things to you which you don't expect, or don't understand. It doesn't seem to make sense; or perhaps they talk a lot but lose the thread of what they are saying. This kind of thing can make communication between you very difficult.

What happens is that the person has lost their ability to think clearly and to keep their thoughts in order. Thoughts become jumbled, so they don't always make sense. Sometimes it seems as though there are too many thoughts and the person feels they can only get rid of them by sharing them with someone, so they may talk endlessly although you may find it hard to follow their meaning. On the other hand, they may suddenly stop talking, because their mind seems to be 'blank'. All this can be very frightening and the person often can't understand what has happened to their thoughts. When this happens, they may spend a lot of time worrying about it and trying to work out what is going on. For instance, they might think that the neighbours are to blame for what is happening, or that you yourselves are being unfriendly towards them. The unusual things they feel sometimes make them believe they are someone special. They cannot be persuaded that this is not true however often you tell them, or try to argue them out of it. To them, all these things are real and they will be convinced by them. This means that the illness changes their whole world and they lose touch with what is really happening.

Another thing that often happens is that the person may hear and sometimes see things which are not there. They may hear noises or voices. Sometimes they understand what they hear; at other times they can make no sense of it at all. They may hear voices talking to them or about them. When this first starts to happen it is often very frightening and people understandably search for an explanation. They are usually able to find some explanation that makes sense to them, for instance that the voices are coming from a transmitter or from the television, or that they are spiritual in nature, from God or angels. Less often people realise that they come from their own mind. These voices can say unpleasant things and the person often talks or shouts back at them, even when other people are present. Occasionally, they may tell them to do things, like opening the front door at night, or to stay awake. They sometime feels they must obey these voices and this can become very distressing.

Schizophrenia can also affect feelings. The person can lose their ability to feel the right emotion at the right time, so that they may laugh about bad news, or may cry when everyone else is laughing. You may have noticed that they do not seem to care for you as they did before, or to show their love for you in the same way. There may be fewer and fewer times when you can really talk to each other and you may sometimes wonder whether they still feel anything for you at all. Your relative can't help all this, because their usual feelings have been swamped by the illness and they have become very wrapped up in themselves. There may be times when they threaten to smash things or to harm someone they are fond of; this is because they are not always in control of how they feel, but are usually quite unaware of the effect this can have on other people. More often, though, they are shy and withdrawn rather than threatening and may be easily upset, particularly if you become irritated by the things that they do.

From time to time the person may realise how much they have changed and how different their life has become. This can make them miserable or desperate and they may say that life is not worth living. Occasionally, they may become very excitable and overactive and say they have no problems at all.

Something else commonly affected by schizophrenia is the amount of energy the person has and their willingness to do things. What usually happens is that the person prefers to be on their own. They may sit in their own room for hours on end listening or talking to voices or pacing up and down. They may hurry through meals, hardly noticing what they eat and then go back to their room. At times they may refuse to eat at all with the family. This happens because they find they can no longer feel at ease with other people – they feel awkward and unable to do or say the right thing. They may even actively avoid other people's company, whereas before they seemed to enjoy it. Some people feel that strangers in the streets stare at them or pass remarks about them and they avoid going out.

Often, the person sleeps a lot of the time and may refuse to get up in the mornings. They may be asleep and awake at completely different times from the rest of the family and this can make it very hard for them to keep a job.

A big problem is when they show little interest in anything and have no idea how to fill the day. Their mind may seem to be a complete blank, or they may pester you to do things to keep them occupied. A lack of energy can cause them to take a long time over such things as housework or a job. This can be very hard to live with.

Finally, many arguments can arise over personal cleanliness, again due to a lack of interest and energy. They may neglect to comb their hair or wash it, refuse to bath or clean their teeth. They may dress unusually or refuse to change their clothes, not bothering about appearances.

Sometimes, being careless about some things, they become unusually fussy about others; they may insist that their room is kept in a certain way, or that you do not disturb their possessions.

These then are some of the general ways in which schizophrenia can affect people, but as we said before, each individual will be affected in a somewhat different way.

Cause and course of the illness

We have mentioned the sorts of things that can happen to someone with schizophrenia. Now we would like to tell you what is known about why the illness appears, the likelihood of further attacks and how it might affect the future.

We now know that inheritance plays some part in the development of schizophrenia but by no means explains fully why the illness appears in a particular person. Just because schizophrenia occurs in one person in a family, it does not necessarily mean that other family members will develop it. Often there are no other relatives at all who have such attacks. Neither does it mean that a person with schizophrenia should not have children because they will be affected. All we do know is that there is an increased risk of schizophrenia for children if a parent has had schizophrenia; one out of ten of these children will develop it in later life.

There are other factors which seem to influence the occurrence of schizophrenia. Research work has been done on many of these factors but at present we can hold no single cause responsible for schizophrenia; there seem to be a number of different contributory factors. We would like to look in detail at one of these causes which may be important for you as members of the same family.

A lot has been written about the influence of the family on schizophrenia. We have no evidence that a family's influence on a child can *cause* schizophrenia. But, once the illness has appeared the family can play an important part in helping the person to stay well. Other features help to decide whether the person will do well, such as their personality and the progress they have made in life before the illness first appears. However, we will concentrate mainly on the part played by the family and will discuss this in more detail later.

Also, we know that the more things a patient has to cope with in life the more likely they are to have an attack. Increased stress can affect anyone badly, but people with schizophrenia seem to be particularly sensitive to it. Changes and conflicts in their lives can also bring on further attacks. We will talk about that later as well.

Well then, what happens to someone who has had schizophrenia? It is important to stress that most people will get better with treatment. They will think more clearly and then many of the unusual ideas will go away. Unfortunately, recovery is not always complete, some people being left with difficulties, but the overall response to treatment is good. With medication, nine out of ten patients stop hearing or seeing things that aren't there and lose their strange beliefs.

About one in four people have an attack of schizophrenia from which they make a complete recovery and then stay well for many years. Others, luckily only a small number, do not respond to treatment at all. However, most patients, although they recover from the attack, are likely to have other attacks. These may occur within weeks of recovery, or may happen years later. During further attacks new kinds of odd behaviour can appear, but often the same pattern will repeat itself.

In between attacks you may notice that your relative is not the same as they were before. For instance they may continue to take a long time to get things done. They may say very little when with other people. They lose interest in things and may be content to sit all day doing nothing. This can lead to difficulties in getting or keeping a job and they may remain unemployed for long periods.

If the person affected does the housework, the family often finds that they cannot manage to do as much as before. Chores remain undone and the house may get neglected. This means that the rest of the family will have to rally round and do more.

Finally, even when well, your relatives may not be as involved in the family as before. They may stay aloof from family events and seem much less affected by them.

These sort of things are not done to annoy you. They are partly the result of the medication, partly due to the illness itself and partly due to the person's own attempts to avoid becoming upset and ill again. However, some of these things improve with time, particularly if the family can manage to be supportive and encouraging.

Treatment

You may have noticed that your relative has been given tablets either while in hospital or after the illness begins if they stay at home. These play an important part in the treatment of schizophrenia. They help to stop the voices in the patient's head, they make them less anxious and restless and help them to think more clearly. They protect them against stresses coming from their own experiences and everyday life.

If drug treatment is started the effects cannot always be seen straight away. It may take days or even weeks before they improve. Even so the tablets have to be taken regularly. They are not like aspirins which you just take when a headache comes on. Some people are not given tablets but are put on injections. These have the same effect as tablets but can be given less often. This is because one injection lasts for several weeks. It is often more convenient for people to have their drug treatment in this way, but again it is important that they have these injections regularly.

Unfortunately, the drugs used for schizophrenia have a number of side-effects. They often make the muscles stiff, or the person may start to shake or feel a physical restlessness, usually in the legs. Reducing the dose may get rid of these side-effects, or the person may need to take another pill which acts as an antidote. There are many different types of medicine which help the person with schizophrenia, and sometimes changing from one type to another will relieve side-effects.

When the person is first treated with drugs, the dose is usually increased until the illness begins to get a bit better. At this stage the drugs often have the effect of making the person quite sleepy. Once the person is recovering, it is possible to reduce the dose, and the sleepiness should improve. However, if it continues once they have returned home, you should inform the doctor, who may then reduce the dose further.

Once medicine has been found helpful, it has to be taken for a long time even when the person feels better. A lot of people find it very hard to stay on their drugs when they feel well, because it seems pointless. Unfortunately, schizophrenia does not usually just go away. Like many of those with diabetes who have to take a daily injection even when feeling well, people with schizophrenia often have to stay on drugs to prevent further attacks and to remain well.

In the same way that there is no sudden improvement when people start drug treatment, there is no sudden change if they stop it. When a person has not taken their tablets or if they have missed an injection, the illness does not return immediately. It can take months until symptoms reappear depending on the amount of difficulties the person has to cope with.

Drug treatment is not the only thing that helps. The atmosphere in the home and the way daily problems are tackled are equally important.

This is because people suffering from schizophrenia are very sensitive to things happening around them. They are much more easily upset than other people by the ups and downs of daily life. Changes in routine can make them feel unsettled and things like moving into a new house or having to face an examination can bring about another attack. When such events can't be avoided it is a good idea to tell the person well in advance if any changes are expected. It is also a good idea to try to manage only one change at a time if at all possible.

Life with a person with schizophrenia can be extremely difficult. They may behave oddly, talk to themselves, spend all day lying in bed and take hours to get things done. This can make you angry and you find you lose your temper. Or you may feel intensely worried and find that you are always wondering where they are and what they will do next. The inevitable questions arise, what happens in the future if things go on like this, how am I going to cope, and you get anxious and upset.

It is not surprising if you find yourself reacting like this. Unfortunately, it is not helpful and can even make things worse. This is because the person with schizophrenia is also easily upset, as we have said, and may find arguments or being fussed over much more difficult than in the past.

The best thing for you to do in this situation is, firstly, not to spend so much time with them so that you don't get on each other's nerves. It is important that the person leads as independent a life as possible. It helps them to gain confidence, to begin to take responsibility and look after themselves again. Sometimes your mental health team will arrange for them to spend the time at a day centre or try to help them find a job. Sometimes, if the person lives with parents, it is a good idea for them to start the normal process of leaving home and living elsewhere, perhaps in a hostel. It may be difficult to accept, but the person actually does better if they live their own life as much as possible. It is also important for the relatives to look after their own needs. You need to spend some time away from the person so that you can develop your own interests, relax and forget about the illness for a while.

Secondly, if you *have* to be together a lot of the time, the best thing to do is not to shout back or get too annoyed by the day-to-day problems. This is easier said than done, but it is helpful for both of you to try to keep a calm atmosphere and to keep the difficulties in some perspective. Talking to other relatives can help with this.

In some families, you and your relatives get very involved with each other; both sides can become extremely worried and upset about everything. The best thing to do about this is to try to let the person make some of their own decisions and for you to let them do this gradually. This can be very hard to do, as it can feel as if you are not caring enough. It can also be a worry that your relative will think you are not interested. However in the long run, it is better for both of you: your relative will find things easier if you care by being less involved and you will find you are feeling less strain.

Most families with a relative with schizophrenia have to solve similar problems. The purpose of these notes is to begin to give you some information, to let you know some of the things you can expect, and some ideas on what you can do to help.

Appendix 2. Helpful Aspects of Therapy form

Your name:

Date of the meeting: **Today's date:**

1. What do you think was *the most helpful* in today's meeting? It might be something you said or did, or something the therapists said or did. Can you say why it was helpful?

2. Did anything else of particular importance happen during this meeting? Include anything else which may have been helpful, or anything which might have been unhelpful.

Appendix 3. Bibliography

References

BROWN, G.W. & RUTTER, M. (1966) The measurement of family activities and relationships: a methodological study. *Human Relations*, **19**, 241–263.

——, BIRLEY, J.L.T. & WING, J.K. (1972) Influence of family life on the course of schizophrenic disorders: a replication. *British Journal of Psychiatry*, **121**, 241–258.

JENKINS, J.H., KARNO, M., DE LA SELVA, A., *et al* (1986) Expressed emotion in cross-cultural context: familial responses to schizophrenic illness among Mexican Americans. In *Treatment of Schizophrenia: Family Assessment and Intervention* (eds M.J. Goldstein, I. Hand & K. Hahlweg). Berlin: Springer Verlag.

LEFF, J.P., KUIPERS, L., BERKOWITZ, R., *et al* (1982) A controlled trial of social intervention in schizophrenic families. *British Journal of Psychiatry*, **141**, 121–134.

——, ——, ——, *et al* (1985) A controlled trial of social intervention in the families of schizophrenic patients: two year follow-up. *British Journal of Psychiatry*, **146**, 594–600.

——, WIG, N.N., GHOSH, A., *et al* (1987) Expressed emotion and schizophrenia in North India. III. Influence of relatives' expressed emotion on the course of schizophrenia in Chandigarh. *British Journal of Psychiatry*, **151**, 166–173.

——, BERKOWITZ, R., SHAVIT, N., *et al* (1989) A trial of family therapy v. a relatives' group for schizophrenia. *British Journal of Psychiatry*, **154**, 58–66.

——, ——, ——, *et al* (1990) A trial of family therapy versus a relatives' group for schizophrenia, two year follow-up. *British Journal of Psychiatry*, **157**, 571–577.

PARKER, G. & HADZI-PAVLOVIC, D. (1990) Expressed emotion as a predictor of schizophrenic relapse: an analysis of aggregated data. *Psychological Medicine*, **20**, 961–965.

TARRIER, N., BARROWCLOUGH, C., VAUGHN, C., *et al* (1988) The community management of schizophrenia: a controlled trial of a behavioural intervention with families to reduce relapse. *British Journal of Psychiatry*, **153**, 532–542.

VAUGHN, C. & LEFF, J. (1976) The influence of family and social factors on the course of psychiatric illness: A comparison of schizophrenic and depressed neurotic patients. *British Journal of Psychiatry*, **129**, 125–137.

——, SNYDER, K.S., JONES, S., *et al* (1984) Family factors in schizophrenic relapse: a California replication of the British research on expressed emotion. *Archives of General Psychiatry*, **41**, 1169–1177.

Further reading

KUIPERS, L. & BEBBINGTON, P. (1990) *Working in Partnership: Clinicians and Carers in the Management of Longstanding Mental Illness*. Oxford: Heinemann Medical.

LAM, D. (1991) Psychosocial family intervention in schizophrenia: a review of empirical studies. *Psychological Medicine*, **21**, 423–441.

LEFF, J. & VAUGHN, C. (1985) *Expressed Emotion in Families: Its Significance for Mental Illness*. New York: Guilford.